Horizons

D1540992

Health 1

Stepping Into Health

Teacher's Guide

Organizer / Writer
Gene Ezell

Major Contributors
Judy Cook, Judy Bredeweg, Dennis Vander Plaats,
Anne VanderWoude, Patricia Knoester, Jesslyn DeBoer

Supervising Editor
Hazel Timmer

Executive Editor
Alan Christopherson

Design and Layout
Leann Kruger

Alpha Omega Publications, Inc. • Rock Rapids, IA

Horizons Health 1 Teacher's Guide

© MMVII by Alpha Omega Publications, Inc.
804 N. 2nd Ave. E., Rock Rapids, IA 51246-1759
All rights reserved.

The framework for this curriculum was provided by:
CHRISTIAN SCHOOLS INTERNATIONAL
3350 East Paris Ave. SE
Grand Rapids, Michigan 49512-3054

Printed in the United States of America

ISBN 978-0-7403-1494-0

CONTENTS

ACKNOWLEDGMENTS

In the summer of 1989, a new health curriculum for Christian schools was planned. That fall a survey of teachers was conducted in grades K-6. The survey indicated that health was becoming an increasingly significant component of the elementary school curriculum. The survey also revealed that Christian school teachers were eager to have materials containing a clear biblical perspective.

Dr. Gene Ezell, a professor of health education at the University of Tennessee at Chattanooga, developed a content outline and scope and sequence for the *Horizons Health* series. He also was the first author of materials for teacher guides.

Many other individuals helped in the preparation of teacher guides for kindergarten, grade one, and grade two. The materials were reviewed and field tested in several schools during the 1990-91 academic year. Also providing input, critiques, and suggestions were Judy Cook, Judy Bredeweg, Dennis VanderPlaats, Anne VanderWoude, Patricia Knoester, and Jesslyn DeBoer.

The publications program was directed by Gordon L. Bordewyk. The supervising editor for *Horizons Health* was Hazel Timmer. Judy Bandstra oversaw production of the materials, and Cheryl Strikwerda Randall created the illustrations.

"I'm Glad" by Carol Greene from *The Little Christian's Songbook*. Copyright © 1975 by Concordia Publishing House. Reprinted by permission of Concordia Publishing House. (Unit 1, Lesson 1)

"Sometimes" from *Rainy Rainy Saturday* by Jack Prelutsky. Copyright © 1974 by Jack Prelutsky. Reprinted by permission of Greenwillow Books, a division of William Morrow and Company, Inc. (Unit 1, Lesson 4)

"We Love" by Ann F. Price from *Rejoice and Sing Praise*. Music copyright © 1966 by Graded Press. Used by permission. (Unit 1, Lesson 6)

"Animal Families" by Lois and Herb Brokering. Copyright © 1970 by Augsburg Publishing House. Reprinted by permission of Augsburg Fortress. (Unit 2, Lesson 2)

"Home, You're Where It's Warm Inside" by Jack Prelutsky from *The Random House Book of Poetry for Children,* Selected and Introduced by Jack Prelutsky. Copyright © 1983 by Jack Prelutsky. Reprinted by permission of Random House, Inc. (Unit 2, Lesson 3)

"Cousin Peter." Reprinted with permission from Mem Fox: *Teaching Drama to Young Children.* (Heinemann Educational Books, Portsmouth, NH: 1987). (Unit 2, Lesson 4)

"Psalm 100" from *Open Thou My Lips* by Betty Ann Ramseth. Copyright © 1969 Augsburg Publishing House. Used by permission of Augsburg Fortress. (Unit 2, Lesson 8)

"I Can" by Lynn Freeman Olson and Joseph W. Insler. Copyright © 1967 by Lutheran Church Press. Reprinted by permission of Augsburg Fortress. (Unit 4, Lesson 1)

"Hands on Shoulders" by Marion Grayson. Reprinted by permission of Robert B. Luce, Inc., c/o IDS, 195 McGregor St., Manchester, N.H. 03102. (Unit 4 Lesson 1)

"What Shall We Do When We All Go Out?" by Fletcher Collins, Jr., from *American Folk Songs for Children* by Ruth Crawford Seeger (Zepher Books). Used by permission. (Unit 4, Lesson 5)

"The Body Engine" from McDonald's *Nutrition Action Pack.* Used by permission. (Unit 5, Lesson 5)

"It's Good to Give Thanks" adapted from Scripture, traditional, arr. Lyndell Leatherman. Copyright © Lillenas Publishing Co. All rights reserved. Used by permission. (Unit 5, Lesson 7)

"Wish" by Dorothy Brown Thompson first published in *Story Parade*, 1944. Used by permission of the author. (Unit 5, Lesson 8)

"White teeth ..." Copyright © by the American Dental Association. Used by permission. (Unit 5, Lesson 10)

"Take Care of Yourself" by Jane Belk Moncure. Copyright © 1973 by The Child's World Inc. Used by permission. (Unit 5, Lesson 11)

"Wear It Every Trip" from *Safety Belts Activity Book.* Copyright © by U.S. Department of Transportation. (Unit 6, Lesson 2)

"Sick." Unable to determine author or source. (Unit 7, Lesson 1)

Role of the Christian School in Health Education

The primary responsibility for educating children belongs to parents. But in the Christian community parents do not have that responsibility alone—church and school also participate in the task of education. The church nurtures the faith of its young members, leading them to understand the implications of faith for their lives. The Christian school teaches children and young people about God's world, equipping them for lives of service. Deriving its authority to educate from the parents who send their children to the school, the Christian school supports and augments instruction provided in the home by teaching all curriculum subjects from a biblical perspective.

One curriculum subject is properly health education. Historically this subject has had low priority in curriculum planning; however, among educators today there is a growing awareness of the importance of health education in a balanced curriculum. Educators are recognizing that in order to promote the well-rounded development of children, the school must give sufficient attention to the healthful living of children as individuals and as members of families and communities. A sequential and comprehensive health education curriculum, such as the *Horizons Health* series, provides the Christian school with the opportunity to deal with basic life issues from a Christian perspective in a consistent way.

The serious health problems facing the contemporary world—the threat of AIDS, the widespread use of recreational drugs, the prevalence of teenage pregnancy, the easy access to abortion—underscore the need for a sound, Christian program of health education. More than ever before students need current, accurate information and clear direction on healthful living. Today's health crises dramatically highlight the obligation of home, church, and school to work together to bring the lordship of Christ to bear on the health education of the community's children.

General Christian Perspective

A Christian perspective on health education begins with the Bible's account of who we are and why we are here. The Bible tells us that we have been created by God in his image. We have been created male and female. We have been created to live in harmony with God, with each other, and with the rest of creation. And we have been assigned the task of caring for God's world.

The Bible has more to tell us. It tells us that because of sin our relationship with God is broken; because of sin we no longer clearly reflect God's image. We live at odds with God and with one another. We don't take care of the created world the way God intended. Even when we try our hardest, we often end up doing the evil we don't want to do (Romans 7:19). And physical death is inevitable.

But that's not the end of our story. In Christ, God has broken the cycle of sin and death. In Christ, God is making us whole. In Christ, God is restoring our relationship to him and to one another. In Christ, we are able to experience the beginning of new life—eternal life—and the hope of a new heaven and earth. We look forward to complete renewal and restoration.

It is this story of redemption history that provides the underlying perspective on health education in the Christian school. When we talk about family life, sexuality, physical fitness, death and dying, and other health topics, it is always in the context of this story.

Christian Perspective and Health Education

Christians believe that God created each human being as an organic unity. The Genesis 2 account of creation says that the Lord God formed man from the dust, breathed into him the breath of life, "and the man became a living being" (verse 7). The Bible does refer to various aspects of the person—such as the mind, flesh, soul, spirit, or heart—but the stress is on the unity of the whole being. The various aspects of a person—the intellectual, emotional, social, spiritual, and physical—are interdependent. In the New Testament the apostle Paul, writing to Corinthian Christians, supports this point of view. Some Corinthians, influenced by their pagan culture, apparently believed that gluttony, drunkenness, or promiscuous sexual activity did not affect their "spiritual" life. Paul counters by strongly denouncing this attitude (1 Corinthians 6: 12-19).

What is the significance of this Christian view of the person for education? It means that health education cannot be treated as incidental to the curriculum. Rather, it must be an integral part of the curriculum at every level. Physical fitness, nutrition, personal health, emotional health, the functioning of body systems—all strands of the health curriculum—affect the whole child. We must recognize that since healthy living affects us in our totality, health education plays a solid role in developing children and equipping them to serve God in the world.

• •

God has given human beings the task of caring for creation. This task includes being caretakers of ourselves. The *Horizons Health* series helps students fulfill their God-given responsibility in several ways. It teaches them about proper personal and dietary health and encourages them to make good choices in these areas. For example, students learn about the different nutritional value in various foods, how family backgrounds and lifestyles influence eating patterns, and the importance of cleanliness in handling and consuming foods. The series also teaches students about personal safety, helping them to handle emergencies and to take precautions to avoid injury and harm. Another strand of *Horizons Health* deals with body systems, and students come to understand how they are "fearfully and wonderfully made." Still another strand deals with disease. In this area students learn, for example, about the defenses which God has provided for our bodies, and how each person can help prevent the spread of disease. The strand of emotional and mental health leads students to develop an honest and healthy self-image concept and to deal with feelings in wholesome ways. Finally, a curriculum strand dealing with substance use and abuse acquaints students with the risks associated with tobacco, alcohol, and drugs.

The Christian view of a person's responsibility to care for himself or herself in order to honor God runs counter to the prevailing view in North American culture. Our culture says that what we do with our body is an individual matter. Sports and fitness are often used for self-glorification, elevating the body to a higher status than it warrants. At the same time, abuse of the body through addiction, inattention to nutrition, or lack of exercise is also common. In a culture such as this, spelling out how we honor God with healthful living and nurturing Christian attitudes toward ourselves and others are crucial for the Christian community.

• •

The Christian's view of death and dying also differs from the view prevalent in society. Christians recognize disease and death as part of sin's effects on creation. Physical death is inevitable, but for those who have new life in Christ, death is not the last word. However, even though Christ has removed death's ultimate sting, death is still the Christian's enemy (1 Corinthians 15: 26, 55).

One strand of the *Horizons Health* series helps students view death and dying from this Christian perspective. In ways appropriate to the developmental levels of the students, the curriculum deals honestly with topics such as fear of death, inevitability of death, and ways Christians cope with death and dying.

• •

Christians are called to reflect God's love in all their relationships. The social health strand of the health curriculum assists students to develop mature Christian attitudes towards others. They also learn interpersonal skills necessary for getting along with others. Thus students are lead to become contributing members of their communities. To answer our deepest needs, God created us to live in relationship with others.

Christians believe that marriage and family are part of a loving God's design for the human race. God, reflecting on his creation, decided that it was not good for Adam to be alone: "I will make a suitable helper for him" (Genesis 2:18). So God established marriage—and by extension, the family—as a cornerstone of creation. As part of God's creation, marriage was very good. The Bible has such a high view of marriage that it uses marriage as a symbol of the relationship of Christ and the Church.

But marriage and family have not escaped the effects of sin. Sin's results are loneliness, alienation, the breaking of family relationships, and the collapse of marriages. In North American society, these effects of sin are also clearly evident. In fact, for some, marriage and the family simply seem outdated institutions that are no longer useful. And pursuing a course of self-fulfillment is held up by many as the highest goal of life.

Christians believe that in Jesus Christ there is healing for brokenness and power to restore family relationships. He calls us to a life of service and responsibility in the family. And although our efforts are imperfect and our homes are not free of trouble, by God's grace family life can be a source of comfort and joy.

The family life strand of the *Horizons Health* series leads students to appreciate the blessings of family life and to assume responsibilities of family membership. Working through family topics—such as resolving conflicts, the importance of basing family life on God's law, knowing how sexuality affects life, and caring for sexuality in a way pleasing to God—helps students to establish basic Christian life patterns, patterns that will have a far-reaching effect on their lives.

● ●

In summary, the *Horizons Health* curriculum seeks to teach Christian students how the lordship of Christ results in healthful living. For only as students acknowledge their accountability to God and form their lives according to his Word are they able to become all their Creator wants them to become and live lives of thankfulness and service.

OVERVIEW

1. *What is Horizons Health?*

Horizons Health is a comprehensive health education curriculum for grades K-8. The series addresses the mental, emotional, social, and spiritual aspects of health as well as the physical. It helps students take responsibility for their health as individuals and as members of families and communities. It gives them opportunity to develop basic life skills—such as communicating, decision making, and resolving conflicts—in order to prepare them to meet the challenges of daily living. Its Christian perspective leads students to recognize that a healthy lifestyle is a lifestyle of obedience to God.

2. *How is the curriculum organized?*

Horizons Health is a flexible curriculum, organized into independent units. The units can be taught in any order, depending on your curriculum needs. Each unit focuses primarily on one or two main strands of the curriculum, with lesser strands integrated where appropriate. These are the eleven strands, which are addressed at each grade level:

Emotional/Mental Health	Nutrition
Social Health/Interpersonal Skills	Disease Prevention
Family Life/Human Sexuality	Safety and First Aid
Growth and Development	Substance Use and Abuse
Personal Health	Consumer Health
Community Health	

The scope and sequence chart shows the topics covered in each strand at this grade level and at the other grade levels of the series.

3. *Do concepts covered in health education overlap with those covered in other content areas?*

Because this is a comprehensive health program rather than a single-topic program, overlap unavoidably occurs in certain content areas. Health education, for example, teaches students about how their bodies work and how substance use and abuse, physical fitness, and nutrition can effect body structures and functions; however, structure and function of body systems may currently be taught in science. Schools may wish to integrate areas that overlap.

4. *What is the personal safety component of Horizons Health?*

At grades K-2 the safety unit includes a lesson on stranger education. In addition, at each level from kindergarten through grade 8 there is one lesson in the safety unit on preventing sexual abuse. In age-appropriate ways, each level deals with differentiating appropriate and inappropriate touch, developing self-protection skills, and identifying sources of help in case of abuse.

Since personal safety is a sensitive area, schools should inform parents about the content of these lessons. Clear communication not only creates trust within the community but also ensures that parents will support and reinforce personal safety concepts taught at school.

Before teaching lessons on personal safety, schools should also develop and adopt a protocol for dealing with suspected or reported abuse. Contact the provincial or state department responsible for child protective services to obtain information and copies of relevant laws. Schools interested in obtaining samples of school policy statements on child welfare that include a protocol for dealing with abuse should contact organizations like the Ontario Alliance of Christian Schools, 617 Garner Road East, Ancaster, Ontario L9G 3K9; or the Society of Christian Schools in British Columbia, 7600 Glover Road, Langley, British Columbia V2Y 1Y1.

5. *What is the sex education component of Horizons Health?*

Sex education is placed within the broader context of family life and human sexuality, one of the strands of the curriculum. Thus at every level *Horizons Health* deals with concepts relating to human sexuality. The grade 5 unit "Growing and Changing" deals specifically with the onset of puberty and the changes it brings.

6. *Is AIDS education included in the health program?*

AIDS education is integrated into the program as part of the disease prevention strand. At levels K-2 there are no AIDS-specific lessons; however, the broader health issues and concepts addressed at these levels—preventing communicable disease, the relationship between personal choices and health, and our God-given responsibility to honor and care for our body—establish the foundation for understanding AIDS-specific concepts at higher grades. At levels 3-6 students learn about AIDS and HIV in age-appropriate ways. Grade 5 material has a lesson on sexually transmitted diseases, including AIDS/HIV.

7. *How can schools best implement a comprehensive health education?*

Planning a strategy to implement the program is crucial for the curriculum to be effective. Three main areas to address are these: keeping parents informed and involved, assisting teachers with resources and training in specialized areas, and providing a school environment that supports the program.

First, parents need to be informed and involved. Because some topics covered in health are controversial, good communication is particularly important. Meeting with parents at the beginning of the year to discuss the content and goals of health education and sending letters home to inform parents about what students are learning and doing in *Horizons Health* (particularly in advance of lessons dealing with sensitive issues) are good basic strategies. Involving parents strengthens the program as health concepts learned at school are reinforced at home.

Second, schools need to provide teachers with resources and training. Many health education curricula have compulsory teacher-training sessions because of the special challenges a comprehensive health education program presents. Some health topics have traditionally not been part of the school curriculum in a formal way, and few teachers have had courses in health education. Thus teachers need opportunities through workshops or in-service training to become comfortable in dealing with sensitive areas such as sexual abuse and substance abuse. In addition, they need resources to support the curriculum and to keep current on health issues. Local or provincial/state agencies and volunteer agencies (for example, the American/Canadian Red Cross or American/Canadian Lung Association) are sources of valuable assistance and offer a wealth of resources. In some cases, inviting experts into the classroom may be advisable.

Third, the total school environment should support the health curriculum and reinforce classroom lessons. Students learn in the classroom about eating snacks that are nutritious and "tooth smart," but does the school ask students to take part in an annual candy sale to raise money for the school? Does the school library contain current materials about a wide variety of wellness issues? What does the climate of the school teach about interpersonal relationships, about living in community? Does the school community model what a Christian community should be? Health education cannot end when students step out of the classroom. Schools need to consider what kind of messages the total environment is sending.

USING HORIZONS HEALTH

The curriculum consists of independent units that can be taught in any order. This flexible design makes it possible for you to choose segments that meet your curriculum needs and your time schedule. The unit summaries found at the beginning of each unit give a quick overview of the unit and help you decide which units or lessons to use.

There are approximately 50 lessons at each of the K-2 levels. With a time schedule of a 30- to 40-minute session for each lesson, *Horizons Health* requires daily sessions for 12 to 14 weeks (or 17-19 weeks teaching three sessions per week and 25-27 weeks teaching two sessions per week). An interdisciplinary program, health lends itself to integration with other subjects, such as Bible, language arts, music, art, science, and social studies. Suggestions for integration are included throughout the curriculum.

Horizons Health provides a carefully planned and comprehensive framework for teaching health education. It is meant to furnish guidelines and suggestions; it is not meant to prescribe each step of each lesson. You are the one to mold and adapt the material and translate it to fit your students and your community.

Format, K-2

The units begin with an overview that includes the following components:

- A *Unit Summary* gives an "at-a-glance" list of lessons.
- *Goals* for the unit are outlined.
- The *Background* provides Christian perspective and/or helpful unit information.
- *Vocabulary* lists words students need to know to understand unit health concepts.
- *Unit Resources* offers suggestions of titles of organizations, books, kits, or audiovisuals helpful as teacher or student resources to support the unit as a whole.
- *Lesson Resources* suggests materials for specific lessons. Most of these resources are listed again in the lesson.

The lessons follow this format:

- *Preparation/Materials* lists what things are needed for the lesson and describes necessary preparations.
- *Objectives* for the lesson are outlined.
- *Background* appears in selected lessons providing specific information on health issues, alerting teachers to sensitive lesson topics, or providing Christian perspective.
- The *Lesson* offers a step-by-step outline. Each lesson ends with a suggestion for closing, providing an opportunity for reflection, self-awareness, summary, or evaluation.
- *Related Activities* presents additional suggestions for student activities, expanding or extending the lesson.

Masters for Teacher Visuals and Student Activity worksheets are located in the back of the Teacher Guide.

Resources

Multimedia resources can significantly increase the impact of the health curriculum, and numerous suggestions for resources have been included. Few health education resources, however, are written from a Christian perspective. Careful screening is necessary before using resources in the classroom. In some cases, you may decide to use selected sections or perhaps to use the materials but add a critical evaluation.

The listings provide suggestions for current resources, but keep in mind that the health field changes rapidly. Although we have included resources that are current at the time of publication, you will need to re-examine and refurbish resources to keep the curriculum up-to-date.

Many community and national volunteer health organizations offer educational materials in their special areas. These materials, which include kits, songs, filmstrips, audiocassettes, lesson plans, activities, posters, student booklets, or brochures for parents, are often available at minimal cost. Many of the materials produced by these organizations are listed in the Unit or Lesson Resources. A list of national health organizations is included at the end of the Introduction. Because new materials are constantly being produced, contacting these health organizations periodically will help you to tap an ongoing source of valuable resources.

Music

Singing together is an activity that builds community. All take part; all share in creating a delightful whole. Singing encourages togetherness, and young children usually enjoy singing and love repeating favorite songs. At the K and 1 levels particularly, *Horizons Health* includes many suggestions for piggyback songs. In addition, a few songs are included in curriculum.

Singing to God is also a natural part of curriculum in the Christian school. God's people of all ages join voices in praise and thanks to God. At the K-2 levels of *Horizons Health*, we have suggested songs that fit with some of the lessons or units. The suggestions are from the following songbooks. If you wish to obtain copies of the books, order them from your local music supplier or directly from the publisher.

Children's Hymnbook. Grand Rapids: Christian Schools International and Eerdmans, 1962.
> Order from Christian Schools International, 3350 East Paris Ave. S.E., Grand Rapids, Michigan 49512; phone 800-635-8288.

Proclaim Songbook 1 and 2. Minneapolis: Augsburg, 1981.
> Order from Augsburg Publishing Co., 426 Fifth St., Box 1209, Minneapolis, Minnesota 19103; phone 800-328-4648.

Psalter Hymnal. Grand Rapids: Christian Reformed Board of Publications, 1986. Order from CRC Publications, 2850 Kalamazoo Ave., Grand Rapids, Michigan 49560; phone 800-333-8300.

Songs of God's Love: A Hymnal for Primary Children. St. Louis: Concordia, 1984. Order from Concordia Publishing House, 3558 S. Jefferson Ave., St. Louis, Missouri 63118; phone 314-664-7000.

Songs to Grow on. Kansas City, Mo.: Lillenas, 1980. Order from Lillenas Publishing Co., P.O. Box 527, Kansas City, Missouri 64141; phone 816-931-1900.

HEALTH EDUCATION RESOURCES

American Alliance for Health, Physical Education, Recreation, and Dance (AAHPERD)
1900 Association Drive
Reston, Virginia 22091
800-321-0789; 703-476-3481

Canadian Association for Health, Physical Education and Recreation (CAHPER)
Place R. Tait McKenzie
1600 James Naismith Drive
Gloucester, Ontario K1B 5N4
613-748-5622
AAHPERD and CAHPER are national organizations committed to promoting health and fitness through a wide variety of programs and publications.

National Clearinghouse for Alcohol and Drug Information
P.O. Box 2345
Rockville, Maryland 20847
800-729-6686
http://ncadi.samhsa.gov

National Family Partnership
2490 Coral Way, Suite 501
Miami, FL 33145
800-705-8997

Office of Disease Prevention and Health Promotion (ODPHP) National Health Information Center
P.O. Box 1133
Washington, D.C. 20012-1133
800-336-4797 or 301-565-4167
Publishes Healthfinder, which lists health education materials (primarily for grades K-6) produced by national and professional organizations. ODPHP provides ordering addresses and prices, but does not evaluate the materials or sources.

Parents Against Drugs (PAD)
70 Maxome Avenue
Willowdale, Ontario M2M 3K1
416-225-6604
Offers current information about drug abuse and a drug awareness workshop for educators.

PRIDE Canada
  Suite 111, Thorvaldson Building
  College of Pharmacy, University of Saskatchewan
  Saskatoon, Saskatchewan S7N 0W0
  800-667-3747

PRIDE, Inc. - United States
  100 Edgewood Avenue, Suite 1002
  Atlanta, Georgia 30303
  800-241-7946
    Parents' Resource Institute for Drug Education (PRIDE) both in Canada and in
    United States and Canada provides drug education resources, training sessions, and
    toll-free hot lines.

U.S. Department of Health and Human Services
  Public Health Service
  Centers for Disease Control
  Center for Chronic Disease Prevention and Health Promotion
  Division of Adolescent and School Health
  Atlanta, Georgia 30333
  404-488-5372
    Offers resource suggestions and updated information about AIDS/HIV. Listed materi-
    als include audiovisuals, books and book chapters, brochures, teaching guides and
    curricula, instructional packages, scripts, and comic books.

SCOPE AND SEQUENCE

	Growth and Development	Disease Prevention	Substance Use/Abuse
K	• growth awareness • five senses and corresponding body parts • primary/secondary teeth	• germs and disease • preventing spread of germs • effect of smoke on lungs	• defining medicine • rule: only adults give medicine • consulting adult before using any unknown substance • choosing a smoke-free environment
1	• review of five senses • naming external body parts • joints • four main organs: brain, heart, stomach, lungs • interrelationship of body parts • growth predictions • primary/secondary teeth	• defining communicable/noncommunicable disease • preventing spread of germs • immunizations • health checkups • effect of smoking on lungs	• differentiating drugs and medicines • symbols for hazardous substances • identifying some drugs
2	• growth awareness • introduction to body systems • function and interdependence of senses • function and basic structure of eyes and ears • visual/hearing impairments	• disease symptoms • defining bacteria and viruses • how germs enter body • effects of nicotine, alcohol, and caffeine on body • identifying eye problems	• identifying common drugs: alcohol, tobacco, and caffeine • products containing caffeine • effect of caffeine on body • how nicotine enters the body • how alcohol affects physical reactions • differentiating prescription and over-the-counter drugs • reasons for using medicine
3	• overview of body systems: skin, muscular, skeletal, digestive, respiratory, circulatory, nervous, excretory (main parts and interrelationships) • growth and development problems (special populations)	• communicable and chronic diseases • AIDS transmission through blood and hypodermic needles • immunizations, proper food storage, and cleanliness as ways to control disease	• defining terms • proper use vs. misuse of substances • influence of advertising on use of over-the-counter medicines • dosages • labels for information • tolerance and addiction • harmful effects of tobacco, smoking
4	• miracle of life • hereditary factors • structure and function of blood • the immune system • hair, skin, and nails • structure and function of teeth • digestive system: parts of, process of digestion • cells/tissues/organs/systems • functions and kinds of cells	• care of skin • diseases of digestive system • lack of nutrients and disease • alcoholism • long term/short term effects of smoking • review HIV transmission through blood, needles	• review of terms: drugs, medicines, substance, prescription, OTC • side effects of medications • avoiding misuse of OTCs • harmful effects of tobacco, alcohol, marijuana, cocaine • defining alcoholism • refusal skills
5	• respiratory system • variations in growth rates • endocrine system • physical, emotional, and social changes of puberty • reproductive system	• main classes of pathogens • chain of infection • some common communicable diseases • preventing respiratory diseases • sexually transmitted diseases, including characteristics, transmission, and prevention of HIV infection	• review of terminology • demonstrating effect of smoking on lungs • refusal skills
6	• fetal development • stages of life • processes by which cells receive nutrients and oxygen: diffusion, filtration, osmosis • review of main body systems, main parts and functions • hereditary and environmental factors • impairments	• preventing cardiovascular disease • risk factors of cardiovascular disease • diseases of muscular, skeletal, and nervous systems • hereditary and environmental factors in disease • alcoholism and cirrhosis • anorexia and bulimia • AIDS/HIV	• chemical dependency and its effects • steroids • results of substance use • societal pressure to use substances • resisting alcohol advertising • strategies for resisting pressure
7/8	• characteristics of stages of life • review of interdependence of body systems • changes of puberty • review of reproductive system • impairments • identifying learning styles	• biblical view of disease • lifestyle choices and disease • eating disorders • suntanning • sexually transmitted diseases, including HIV/AIDS • review reducing risk of communicable and acquired diseases • understanding reality of health problems	• alcohol, tobacco, drug abuse (student research) • decision-making and refusal skills

	Nutrition	Emotional/Mental Health	Social Health/Interpersonal Skills
K	• food for energy and growing • plant and animal food sources • eating a variety of foods	• created unique • differences and similarities • main feelings • situations and feelings • responding to others' feelings	• minding manners • manners and feelings • listening to each other • ways to share • cooperating
1	• food and body energy • five food groups • eating from all food groups • eating healthy snacks • diet and tooth health	• created unique • alike and different • naming and exploring feelings • body language • dealing with feelings • ways to deal with anger • developing empathy	• purpose of good manners • practicing good manners • active listening steps • sharing • practicing cooperation
2	• five food groups • limiting extras • daily serving requirements • balanced eating • cleanliness and food handling • eating breakfast • smart snacks for teeth	• identifying individual gifts/interests • blessing others with our gifts • review of main feelings • identifying a variety of feelings • feelings and actions • communicating feelings • developing empathy • saying no and feelings	• communicating with others • developing social skills/manners • showing appreciation • helping others • active listening • selfish/unselfish attitudes • importance of cooperating
3	• classifying foods • combination foods • define nutrients needed for growth, maintenance, repair of body • limited nutritional value of some foods • healthy snacks • diet and tooth decay	• self-awareness and acceptance • appreciating diversity • identifying and expressing feelings • emotions and body feelings • how feelings affect thoughts and actions • dealing with specific emotions: fear, hurt, anger, being left out • humor and feelings	• developing friendships • factors that affect friendships • kinds of friendships • showing kindness toward others • laughing with, not at • active listening • resolving conflicts
4	• six major classes of nutrients: fats, carbohydrates, water, minerals, vitamins, protein • function of nutrients • serving size • lack of nutrients and disease • good food, good times	• self-knowledge and knowledge of God • being saints and sinners • individual differences as part of God's plan • using gifts to serve • how others affect self-concept • showing appreciation for others • handling and expressing feelings • avoiding self-putdowns • making decisions	• belonging to groups other than family • showing respect for others • accepting differences • communication skills • working out problems in interpersonal relationships
5	• review of main nutrients and their sources • vitamins, minerals, and their functions • function of water • individual nutrition requirements • nutrition deficiencies and health • influences on eating patterns	• growing up • identifying individual strengths • range of feelings • developing feelings vocabulary • ways of dealing with emotions • expressing feelings without blaming • overall wellness and emotions • dealing with anger in healthy ways	• wise ways in relationships (Proverbs) • forgiveness and maintaining friendships • respecting others • resolving conflicts • social skills • cooperative skills
6	• criteria for proper food selection • diet analysis • nutrients: carbohydrates, proteins, fats • reducing salt and sugar • results of unbalanced diet • eating disorders	• new life in Christ • patterns of life: inherited and acquired characteristics • handling ups and downs of feelings • interaction of feelings, thoughts, and actions • identifying and managing stress • recognizing influences • decision making and peer influence	• identifying social support network • factors that build up or break down relationships • erecting barriers: prejudice, discrimination, labeling • communication: basic elements, verbal/nonverbal, active listening • deciding to care about others
7/8	• proper nutrition and dieting	• identifying self as God's image bearer and God's child • being made new in Christ • self-talk and self-confidence • discovering, accepting, and developing gifts • using gifts to serve God/community • influence of media on self-concept • decision-making values/strategies • setting goals • developing study skills • being assertive • recognizing and expressing feelings	• biblical view of community • types of love • living in community • dealing with internal/peer pressure • using peer pressure positively • friendship • dealing with conflict • communication

	Family Life/Human Sexuality	Personal Health	Community Health
K	• families—part of God's plan • similarities/differences among families • gender differences • feelings and family • our families and God's family • dealing with death	• good health choices • dressing to stay healthy • exercise and rest • cleanliness and health • care of teeth: brushing and checkups	• health helpers • smoke in environment
1	• living things reproduce • families—part of God's plan • kinds of families • contributing to family life • family changes • death and Christian hope • Christian families in context of God's family	• making healthy choices • staying fit • eating from all food groups • tooth care: plaque, brushing, checkups, diet • grooming and health	• defining pollution • causes of air pollution • health helpers • immunizations
2	• families provide basic needs • human sexuality, a gift of God • exploring gender differences/similarities • resolving conflicts • family rules • new beginnings and forgiveness • family heritage and traditions • dealing with death	• good health habits • keeping fit and active • avoiding too much TV • getting enough sleep • eating a balanced diet • eating healthy snacks and breakfast • review of good grooming habits • tooth care: brushing, flossing, snacks	• noise pollution
3	• God's law of love as the basis of family living • depending on family members • communicating in families • living patterns and culture • life cycle and the family • sexual identity, an integral part of a person • dealing with death	• benefits of fitness • being physically fit; flexibility, endurance, strength • good posture • oral hygiene • eating healthy foods • benefits of sleep	• health agencies • role of community workers in safety
4	• institution of marriage/family • responsibility and family life • family and the wider community • communicating • death and dying	• components of personal health • building physical fitness • importance of cleanliness • posture • sleep and rest	• effect of contaminated food, water, air
5	• wellness in family relationships • family's impact on members' development • foundation of marriage • changes during puberty • authority/freedom in family life • coping with change in family life • death and dying	• concept of wellness • review of personal health practices • keeping a healthy balance • inventory of health habits • fitness and overall health • exercise and respiratory endurance	• air pollution • water pollution and health • community health resources
6	• stages of life/development • courtship, marriage intimacy • beginning of human life • fetal development and birth process • being a Christian family • societal pressures and family life • changes in adolescence and family life • death/dying	• healthy lifestyle • benefits/components of fitness • weight, strength, posture, obesity, losing healthfully • care of skin, eyes, and ears • importance of sleep/rest • oral hygiene • personal cleanliness/disease prevention • setting health goals	• community problems caused by substance abuse • treatment for alcoholism • community health resources
7/8	• family life • sexuality vs. sex • biblical view of sexuality • myths of sex and sexuality • changes in puberty • chastity and abstinence • healthy male-female relationships • sexual abuse	• healthy lifestyle choices • influence of fashion on ideas of beauty • dieting and health • physical fitness and overall wellness • review components of health fitness • review personal hygiene concepts	• community resources for getting help for substance abuse/other health problems

	Consumer Health	Safety/First Aid
K		• rules and safety • poison safety • medicine and safety • traffic safety • strangers and safety • fire safety: basic rules • emergency phoning • appropriate/inappropriate touch
1	• health checkups	• medicine safety • poison safety: basic rules and household poisons • safety and strangers • review of fire safety • car passenger safety • dealing with emergencies • appropriate/inappropriate touch
2	• aid for visual and hearing impaired	• care of eyes and ears • review of stranger education • intro. to bike safety • review of fire safety • home escape plan • seatbelts • emergency phoning • preventing sexual abuse: appropriate/inappropriate/confusing touch • good and bad secrets
3	• influence of ads on use of substances • labels as a source of information • reasons for using common health products	• risk-taking • bicycle safety • water safety • electrical appliances • preventing sexual abuse: appropriate/ inappropriate touch, trickery, self-protection, sources of help • action plan for an emergency • first aid: scrapes, nosebleeds, burns, blisters
4		• accidents—emotional, decisional factors • review of basic safety rules • playground safety • bicycle safety • fire safety, flame hazards • home alone • preventing sexual abuse: definition, touch continuum, self-protection
5	• advertising and food choices	• taking responsibility for safety of self and others • basic emergency first aid • rescue breathing • preventing sexual abuse: defining sexual abuse, saying no assertively, sources of help
6	• getting correct health care	• taking responsibility for safety of self and others • safety in extreme hot or cold weather • safety and natural disasters • review of basic safety rules • home hazard check • defining/preventing sexual abuse: • self-protection, sources of help
7/8	• evaluating advertisements • media sales techniques	• review of basic safety and first aid • responding in emergencies • preventing sexual abuse • identifying and practicing self-protection skills

Unit 1

Getting to Know Myself

Goals

- Students will develop a healthy self-awareness.
- Students will develop respect for others' uniqueness and feelings.
- Students will develop their understanding of the role of feelings.
- Students will choose to express feelings in a healthy and responsible way.

Background

Emotional and mental health is the focus of this unit. In it students examine the topic of feelings and recognize more clearly what prompts certain feelings. They learn about handling and expressing their emotions in healthy ways and how to respond in healthy ways to the emotions of others.

What are healthy ways for Christians to deal with emotions? Mary Vander Goot in her book *Healthy Emotions: Helping Children Grow* cautions against two extremes. On one extreme are Christians who promote the idea that good children will have only "nice" feelings. Much popular Christian literature and art promote this idea by picturing only smiling, sweet children. Vander Goot warns that "if we fall into the habit of thinking that pleasant emotions are good and unpleasant emotions are bad, and if we consequently elect to cover up negative emotions rather than attend to them, learn from them, and grow from them, we lose integrity and become emotionally artificial." Showing sadness, fear, or anger is not un-Christian. However, in reaction to this "saccharine" approach, some Christians have gone to the opposite extreme, maintaining that children should have the freedom to express whatever they feel. This approach is dangerously irresponsible. For although disturbing emotions should not be stifled or denied, randomly expressing emotions with no concern for others or failing to deal with their causes is also not healthy.

To deal with emotions in a healthy way we must recognize and express the rich variety of human emotions. But we must also learn to control our emotions, to act on them responsibly. Vander Goot puts it this way: "Although our emotions are woven in with our actions, they are counselors to our actions but not their dictators. Our emotions give us a strong sense of our condition; however, we must make insightful and responsible decisions when we act to alter our condition."

To stay emotionally healthy takes maintenance. Vander Goot singles out three goals to work toward: richness, fit, and control. The first goal, richness, means being able to express a wide variety of feelings. Many people live impoverished emotional lives. Although there are many reasons for this, sometimes family and societal patterns are the cause. Some families, for example, don't allow open expressions of appreciation, affection, or fear; society frowns upon men expressing fear or sadness and upon women expressing anger. A narrow emotional life has wide implications because it keeps us from understanding the emotions of others and thus affects our relationships with others. Fit, the second goal, has to do with how emotions connect with events. Emotions must be fitting; they need to be appropriate to an event. "A pleasant feeling in the face of a horrid event is false, and despair in the presence of great possibilities is equally false," comments Vander Goot. We have a choice as to how to express our feelings. The goal is to work toward fitting emotions and fitting expressions of emotion. Control, the third goal, requires a purpose in life, something to give our lives direction. Only in the light of that purpose or commitment are we able to assess our emotional life and work toward reflecting that commitment in our emotions. The goal of control is not to stifle emotions, but to follow up on emotions "wisely so that our feelings, our relationships, our actions, and our perceptions move toward greater and greater integrity."

Christ, whose kingly rule includes our emotional life, calls us to be his disciples, to live according to the laws of the kingdom of God. By God's grace we can learn to become aware of the meaning of our feelings and to act on them in ways that lead us and our neighbors to emotional health.

Vocabulary

Integrate the following suggested vocabulary:

unique	feelings	healthy	lonely	ashamed
create	right	emotions	jealous	disappointed
angry	wrong	joyful	worried	bless/blessing
sad	situation	calm	silly	body language
happy	dangerous	confused	excited	mean
afraid	surprised	loving	frustrated	embarrassed

Unit Resources

All Together: Our Multicultural Community. Kit. National Film Board of Canada, 1984.
This kit, which includes two filmstrips, audiocassettes (*All My Colours* and *All My Friends*) and a teacher guide, aims to develop tolerance and acceptance of differences both cultural and individual.

Borba, Michele and Craig. *Self-Esteem: A Classroom Affair.* Volumes 1 and 2. San Francisco: Harper, 1984 and 1985.
Contains ideas for activities and reproducible worksheets.

Canfield, Jack, and Harold C. Wells. *100 Ways to Enhance Self-Concept in the Classroom: A Handbook for Teachers and Parents.* Englewood Cliffs, N. J.: Prentice-Hall, 1976.
This classic contains suggestions for building an environment of positive support, increasing student self-awareness, and improving relationships with others.

Joosse, Wayne. *The Christian's Self-Image: Issues and Implications.* Occasional Papers from Calvin College. Grand Rapids: Calvin College, 1989.
A critical look at the self-esteem movement.

Meagher, Laura. *Teaching Children About Global Awareness.* Lexington, N.Y.: Crossroad, 1991.
Meagher offers valuable suggestions for promoting global awareness in children.

Prelutsky, Jack, compiler. *The Random House Book of Poetry for Children.* New York: Random House, 1983.
A good source of poetry that honestly expresses children's feelings. Some suggestions: "Wrestling" by Kathleen Fraser, "Keziah" by Gwendolyn Brooks, "When I Was Lost," by Dorothy Aldis, "Sulk" and They're Calling" by Felice Holman.

The Pine Tree Club. Videocassette. Grand Rapids: Pine Rest Life Enrichment Center, 1988.
Intended for grades K-4, this 36-minute video teaches these rules of positive behavior: everyone is equal; it's o.k. to be different; respect others; say "no" when something is wrong; express feelings in a responsible way. To order, contact the Pine Rest Life Enrichment Center, 300 68th St. S.E., Grand Rapids, Michigan 49508.

Prutzman, Priscilla, and others. *The Friendly Classroom for a Small Planet.* Philadelphia: New Society Publishers, 1988.
This resource is put out by Children's Creative Response to Conflict, an organization with Quaker roots. It contains suggestions/activities for building community, learning to communicate, promoting self-awareness and empathy. Order from the publisher: P.O. Box 582, Santa Cruz, California 95061.

Sofield, Juliano and Hammett. *Design for Wholeness: Dealing With Anger, Learning to Forgive, Building Self-Esteem.* Notre Dame, Ind.: Ave Maria Press, 1990.
Written from Christian (Roman Catholic) perspective, this resource contains helpful background material for teachers.

Vander Goot, Mary. *Healthy Emotions: Helping Children Grow.* Grand Rapids: Baker, 1987.
Written from a solid Christian perspective, this resource is "about normal emotions of normal children." The author's purpose is to help adults deal effectively with children's emotions. In chapter 7, "Teachers and School," Vander Goot reflects on the way the school environment influences the emotional development of children.

You, Me, and Others—Variety. White Plains, NY: March of Dimes, 1985.
This resource, which is part of the March of Dimes' curriculum on genetics, has five lessons that explore variations among individuals: (1) "Is It Alive? (2) "We Are Alike & Different," (3) "How Tall?" (4) "What Do I Like?" (5) "My Body." Suggested learning activities are listed for each grade level, and 5 activity masters are included. Contact the local chapter of March of Dimes to obtain the materials.

Lesson Resources
Lesson 1
Ideas, Thoughts, and Feelings. Audiocassette. Educational Activities.
"I Like Me" and "I Don't Like Me" are two songs that tie in with the lesson.

Lungs Are for Life - 2. Kit. American Lung Association, 1983.
This kit includes a teacher guide, activity sheets, and two posters (one entitled: "Taking Off: Looking at Our Feelings"). Although the focus of the material is healthy lungs, the main concept of the opening unit, Getting to Know You, is self-awareness. Contact the local chapter of the American Lung Association to find out how to obtain the kit.

Sharmat, Marjorie. *Helga High-Up.* New York: Scholastic, 1987.
Helga the giraffe learns to appreciate herself.

Stouse, Karla F. *Different Is Kind of Nice.* St. Meinrad, Ind.: Abbey, 1987.
For grades 2 and up.

Spier, Peter. *People*. New York: Doubleday, 1980.
  Detailed illustrations picture the wide diversity of people.

Lesson 2
Aliki. *Feelings*. New York: Greenwillow, 1984.

Berger, Terry. *I Have Feelings*. Human Science Press, 1971.
  A 40-page book exploring 17 different feelings and situations that evoke each. Photographs help children identify the feelings.

Cohen, Miriam. *Jim's Dog Muffins*. New York: Greenwillow, 1984.
  Jim feels sad when his pet Muffins dies.

Fernandes, Eugenie. *A Difficult Day*. Toronto: Kids Can Press, 1987.
  Melinda is feeling grouchy until her mother's freshly-baked cookies turn things around.

Fiday, Beverly and David. *Time to Go*. New York: Harcourt, 1990.
  A child sadly says goodbye to the family farm.

Kachenmeister, Cherryl. *On Monday When It Rained*. Boston: Houghton, 1989.
  A boy tells about what happened each day of the week, and photographs show how he felt each day.

Krasilovsky, Phyllis. *The Shy Little Girl*. Topeka, Kansas.
  Anne and Claudia who are both shy, become friends. It gradually becomes easier for them to join in with their classmates.

Moss, Marissa. *Regina's Big Mistake*. Boston: Houghton, 1990.
  Regina's feelings about a drawing assignment that goes wrong will be familiar to all children.

Murphy, Elspeth. *Sometimes I Have to Cry: Verses from the Psalms on Tears*. Weston, Ont./Elgin, Ill.: Cook, 1988.

_____. *Sometimes I Think "What If?" Psalm 46 for Children*. Weston, Ont./Elgin, Ill.: Cook, 1987.
  A child imagines a series of disasters but finds peace knowing that God is in charge and "right here."

Simon, Norma. *I Am Not a Cry Baby*. Niles, Ill.: Whitman, 1989.
  It's all right to cry because often there are good reasons for crying.

Tester, Sylvia. *Moods and Emotions*. Marvel Education.
  A set of 16 dramatic pictures portraying emotions such as love, joy, anger, fear, sorrow, satisfaction, frustration and protectiveness. Accompanied by a 40-page manual of suggestions for classroom use.

Viorst, Judith. *Alexander and the Terrible, Horrible, No Good, Very Bad Day*. New York: Macmillian, 1972.

Williams, Marcia. *Not a Worry in the World*. New York: Crown, 1990.
  A lighthearted book that helps children laugh at some common worries.

Lessons 3 and 4
Aliki. *We Are Best Friends*. New York: Greenwillow, 1982.

Borgeois, Paulette. *Franklin in the Dark.* Toronto: Kids Can Press, 1986.

_____. *Franklin Fibs.* Toronto: Kids Can Press, 1991.

Cohen, Miriam. *Jim Meets the Thing.* New York: Greenwillow, 1981.

DeJong, Meindert. *Nobody Plays With a Cabbage.* New York: Harper, 1962.

Greenfield, Eloise. *She Come Bringing Me That Little Baby Girl.* New York: Harper, 1990.

Grimes, Nikki. *Something on My Mind.* New York: Dutton, 1978.

Hayes, Sarah. *Mary, Mary.* New York: McElderry, 1990.
    A little girl responds to a giant's loneliness.

Keats, Ezra Jack. *The Trip.* New York: Morrow, 1987.

Marshall, James. *What's the Matter With Carruthers?* Boston: Houghton, 1972.

Munsch, Robert. *Mortimer.* Willowdale, Ont.: Annick Press, 1983.

Murphy, Elspeth. *God Cares When I'm Feeling Mean.* Weston, Ont./Elgin, Ill.: Cook, 1985.

Schindler, Regine. *A Miracle for Sarah.* Nashville: Abingdon, 1985.

Sharmat, Marjorie. *Bartholomew the Bossy.* New York: Macmillan, 1984.

_____. *Attila the Angry.* New York: Holiday, 1985.

Simon, Norma. *How Do I Feel?* Niles, Ill.: Whitman, 1970.

_____. *I Was So Mad!* Niles, Ill.: Whitman, 1974.

Skorpen, Liesel. *His Mother's Dog.* New York: Harper, 1978.

Wittels, Harriet, and Joan Greisman. *Things I Hate!* New York: Human Sciences Press, 1973.

Zolotow, Charlotte. *The Quarreling Book.* New York: Harper, 1963.

_____. *The Hating Book.* New York: Harper, 1969.

_____. *It's Not Fair.* New York: Harper, 1976.

Lesson 5

Berenstain, Stan and Jan. *The Berenstain Bears and the Double Dare.* New York: Random, 1988.

Hazen, Barbara. *Just Say No.* Golden Look-Look Books. New York, Western Publishing, 1991.

Murphy, Elspeth. *Sometimes I'm Good, Sometimes I'm Bad.* Weston, Ont./Elgin, Ill.: Cook, 1981.

LESSON 1: CREATED TO BE ME

Preparation/Materials

- Make two puppets (Sam and Terry) to use throughout the year in health class. Sock puppets may be the easiest to make and manipulate. Choose contrasting colored (bright or pastel) socks for the puppets; add felt facial features and yarn hair.
- Plan/practice a brief puppet monologue introducing health class.
- White or manila construction paper, one sheet per student
- A couple of small, unbreakable mirrors or one large, mounted mirror
- Optional: teacher's self-portrait to use as a model
- Optional: additional songs on theme of individual uniqueness

Objectives

- Students will recognize that God made each person unique.
- Students will identify their own unique characteristics.
- Students will react with thanksgiving to God.

Background

The self-esteem movement has been the center of vigorous debate in recent years. Floods of articles, books, and films have been produced on the importance of a positive self-image and the disastrous results of a negative self-image. Wayne Joosse in *The Christian's Self-Image: Issues and Implications* points out that Christians have climbed onto the self-esteem bandwagon. They see in the movement a synthesis of biblical truth and psychological health, which offers a long-overdue correction to the negative image of the self prevalent in Christian tradition. Other Christians, however, resist promoting self-esteem. In their view, promoting self-esteem is promoting pride and ignoring the sin in each of us. They charge that the self-esteem movement exemplifies the narcissism of North American culture.

Although clearly Christians must critically evaluate the self-esteem movement, there is little question that how children see themselves is extremely important. Educators have found a direct relationship between self-esteem and success in school. And health educators have found that children with poor self-concept are more likely to take part in unhealthy and risky behaviors. Teachers are abdicating their responsibility if they ignore the importance of self-esteem. Indeed, teachers along with parents are the ones chiefly responsible for shaping self-image in young children.

This lesson provides a framework for creating a classroom in which student differences are recognized and accepted. Tell students, "God created each of you in his image. You are God's child, and God loves you just the way you are."

Because puppetry is an ideal way to present many of the situations dealt with in health, we are suggesting that you make two "health" puppets. Try to create a distinctive personality for each puppet. Make them into class friends, humorous or wise commentators, or cheerful comforters. And consider using them outside of health class to resolve problems that may arise between students. Of course, if you find puppets difficult to use, you may prefer to act out the scenes yourself or rely more heavily on children's literature.

Lesson

1. Use one of the puppets to introduce the health class in a lively, friendly way. Have the puppet express excitement about coming to the classroom because there are all kinds of things to discover about ourselves and others in health.

    Script starter:

    > Sam: Well, here I am. Do you know who I am? I'm Sam, and I'm a puppet. Did you ever see a puppet just like me before? No? I'm not surprised, because I'm a one-of-a-kind puppet. I'm unique. (Have puppet point out its unique features or ask the class to identify them.) Say, do you know why I'm here? I'm a health puppet. I'm going to help you learn things that will help you be healthy.

    Continue the monologue and have the puppet describe how it will contribute to health class (tell stories, answer questions, and listen to what the class has to say). End the monologue by having the puppet look around the classroom and comment on the variety of children in the classroom: "Hey, I thought I was special, but so are all of you!"

    Pick up on the puppet's last comment and ask the class what they think it meant. Use their response to lead into step 2.

    Alternative option: omit the puppet monologue and begin the lesson with the discussion in step 2.

2. Lead students in a discussion of the uniqueness of each individual. Emphasize that God created each one of us special and loves each of us. Teach the word *unique*.

3. Praise and thank God for making us unique. Teach and sing "I'm Glad." Other songs on the lesson theme are: "There's No One Exactly Like Me" (*Songs to Grow On*, 57), and "If I Were a Butterfly" (*Songs of God's Love*, 58; *Proclaim Songbook 1*, 14).

4. **Student activity.** Have the class draw or paint self-portraits at a center. Provide a few small mirrors or one large, mounted mirror that students can use to study themselves. Encourage them to include in their portraits individual features such as freckles, dimples, high foreheads, round cheeks, and glasses. Post your own self-portrait to create student interest and to provide a model.

    Try to establish a classroom climate in which individual differences are accepted. Stress that each of us is differently gifted. Be particularly sensitive to students with impairments, but keep the focus for all students on abilities rather than disabilities.

    Take the time to let children talk about their self-portraits before displaying them. You may wish to mat the pictures to give the portraits a more finished look.

5. **Closure:** "Today we learned that each of us is unique. There's not another person exactly like me or like you in the world. That's the way God made us, and God loves each of us—just the way we are."

Related Activities

1. Single out each class member for special attention in some way. Have a "special person of the week" or schedule birthday activities that focus on each child's special gifts.

2. Center idea: have students make posters about themselves. Each student can put the self-portrait in the center of the poster and then draw 5-10 things that make him or her unique. Let volunteers share their posters. If students are having difficulty with the activity, let them take the posters home to have family members help them with ideas. Or such a poster could be completed in advance by the person of the week and mounted in a "superstar" display.

3. Students can create rainbows reflecting their uniqueness. Make an activity sheet with a rainbow of four or five segments for each child to color. Label the segments with letters or numbers. Direct students to color each segment to reflect an individual difference (for example, color of hair, eyes, skin, an item of clothing, or favorite color). Have them write "I am unique" over the rainbow. Consider tape recording the directions and making this a center activity.

4. Journal idea: have the students write the heading, "God has given me a special gift." Ask each student to write three or four lines about special interests or talents (examples: fast runner, good collector, expressive reader, nice singing voice).

5. Read books related to the lesson theme. *Something Special* by David McPhail, *All About Me* by Melanie and Chris Rice, and *All I Am* by Eileen Roe are a few suggested titles.

I'm Glad

German folk tune

Carol Greene

LESSON 2: WE ARE ALIKE—WE ARE DIFFERENT

Preparation/Materials
- Health puppets
- Plan a puppet script about alike/different concept.
- Student Activity page
- Optional: song from previous lesson

Objectives
- Students will understand the concepts of alike and different.
- Students will identify similarities and differences among themselves.
- Students will recognize and appreciate the diversity of God's creation.

• •

Lesson (2 sessions)

1. Use the puppet Sam to briefly review concepts of previous lesson. ("Let's see; what did we talk about? I remember. We talked about being unique. Mmmm … unique … I don't remember what that means, do you?" Elicit the meaning from the class.)

Through a puppet dialogue explain the concept of alike/different.

Dialogue suggestion:

> Sam: This is my friend Terry. Terry is a health puppet, too. You'll like Terry. Terry likes to play games. And Terry is a kind person.
> Terry (whispering to Sam): Sam, Sam …
> Sam (whispering to Terry): What the matter? Don't interrupt. I'm introducing you to the class.
> Terry: I'm getting embarrassed, Sam.
> Sam (to class): And sometimes Terry's a little shy, too.
> Terry: Well, that's the way I am. Once I know the boys and girls better, I won't be shy anymore.
> Sam: That's okay, Terry. I like standing up here and talking.
> Terry: It's funny that we're such good friends. We're so different from each other.

Interrupt the dialogue and ask the class to identify ways the puppets are different from each other, both in appearance and personality. Then have students tell how the puppets are alike.

> Terry: Sam, I've been thinking … do you know the story of Pinocchio? He was a puppet made of wood, but one day he changed and then he could do all the things boys and girls could. Do you think we could change like that?
> Sam: Naw. That's just a story. How could we ever start breathing and talking and walking?
> Terry: But Sam, then we could play games with the boys and girls. We could eat pizza, too.
> Sam: Just enjoy being a puppet, Terry. That's fun, isn't it?

Ask the class to compose and contrast the puppets with themselves. How are they different from the puppets? Are they alike in any way?

As an alternative to the puppet dialogue, compare/contrast two well-known cartoon characters, two characters from a favorite class book, or two children in a magazine picture.

2. Teach the words *alike* and *different.* Brainstorm a list of ways God has made everyone in the class alike (in physical appearance, basic body parts, survival needs, ability to talk, sing, think, and so on) and ways in which they are made different (color of eyes, curly or straight hair, dimples, freckles, size, voice). Again, use the activity to establish a classroom climate of acceptance, and be sensitive to physical impairments.

3. Celebrate the diversity of God's creation. Have students imagine what the class would be like if the members all looked alike. Enjoy singing some of the songs from the previous lesson.

4. Play a kind of Simon Says game to stimulate students to identify similarities and differences. Gather the class into a circle. Then give instructions such as the following:
   • Clap if you have two hands.
   • Blink your eyes if they are brown.
   • Touch your chin if you have dimples.
   • Raise your hand if you are a girl.

5. **Student activity.** Students should complete a "special person" award. Instruct them to write their name on the line provided. Ask children to give reasons they are special. If they are having trouble coming up with an idea, invite their peers to offer suggestions. The class members can then note similarities and differences in their gifts.

6. **Closure:** "Each one of us is unique. In some ways each of us is different from others. But we're the same as others, too! How are we the same? (Elicit suggestions.) One important way we're the same is this: God created us, and we are God's children."

Related Activities

1. This is a good opportunity to increase students' sensitivity to people who are differently abled. Together read and discuss a story about a child with an impairment: *I Have a Sister, My Sister Is Deaf* by Jeanne W. Petersen, *Peter Gets a Hearing Aid* by Nigel Snell, *My Sister Kate: How She Sees God's World* by Christine Wright, or one of the other excellent books currently available.

2. Bind the self-portraits from the previous lesson into a class book. Encourage the students to read the book, looking for things that they have in common as well as things that make them unique.

3. Have each class member make an "All About Me" booklet. The self-portrait from Lesson 1 could be the first page. Subsequent pages could include hand-tracings, drawings of favorite animals or foods, and a writing activity on "something I can do." Read *All I Am* by Eileen Roe and *God Makes Us Different* by Helen Caswell.

LESSON 3: FOUR MAIN FEELINGS

Preparation/Materials

- Make a poster of faces showing four basic feelings:

afraid   sad

angry   happy

- Plan a teacher skit for depicting all four emotions.
- For student posters:
  tagboard, one piece for each pair or group
  Divide each poster into four columns and draw one feelings face as a heading for each column.
  magazines, newspapers, old coloring books
- Optional: chart paper

Objectives

- Students will identify/review four basic feelings.
- Students will conclude that all people have feelings.
- Students will infer feelings from body language and facial expression.

Background

Our body language sends emotional messages to others. Mary Vander Goot reminds us that we don't *have* bodies, we *are* our bodies, and "our emotions take hold of us bodily."

When we look down, cover our face with our hands, or scrunch ourselves together, we are expressing an emotion—fear. And when we talk, our tone of voice can subtly communicate whether we are friendly or distant, whether we approve or disapprove. For this reason, teachers should take the time to critique their body language in the classroom. Ask yourself: Is the way I am presenting myself likely to elicit the response I wish to have from the children?

Vander Goot suggests that teachers should think about ways to emotionally contact specific children. Great disparity of demeanor between the teacher and certain children may create barriers. She suggests trying to make contact through empathetic body language: "It is much easier to admit sadness to an adult whose voice, face, or posture says that this is someone who also knows what sadness is."

This last suggestion highlights one way this and subsequent lessons on feelings can serve to help children deal with their emotions. Many children believe that they are the only ones who have certain feelings. Talking about feelings and recognizing that others have the same feelings can be liberating. Vander Goot states that "one of the first steps to managing emotions is admitting to having them," and she notes that "students, who in the process of social comparison become convinced that they are the only ones who have felt the way they do, spend a good deal of their energy hiding their feelings from others and sometimes even from themselves." On the other hand, knowing that others grapple with similar emotions gives students valuable support and promotes mental and emotional health.

• •

Lesson

1. Act out the four basic emotions in a one-person skit or pantomime. Stop at appropriate points, and ask the class to identify which emotion is being depicted. Lead students to specify how they identified the emotion (clues in facial expression, posture, and/or tone of voice).

2. Use the four faces poster to identify and discuss, by turn, each of the four main feelings. For example, point to the face showing fear, ask students to identify the feeling, and point out how the mouth and other facial features often look when a person is afraid. Have class members show you how they may look and act when they feel afraid.

   Ask students to identify some things that make them afraid. ("Have you ever felt afraid? What made you feel that way?") List their responses—either on the poster or on a separate chart.

   Follow the same procedure for each feelings face. During the discussion, make the point that feelings can change rapidly and that sometimes a person may have more than one feeling about something or someone. (Example: a person may feel happy to be asked to sing in a program, but may also feel a little afraid to sing.) Also lead the class to understand that although body language helps us guess how people feel, we can't be sure unless we ask. (In the next lesson, students practice asking about feelings.) Stress that all people, young and old, have these feelings and that the feelings themselves are neither good or bad.

   Display the poster and the lists. Add to the lists as the unit progresses.

3. **Student activity.** Have class members work in pairs or in groups to make posters illustrating the four main feelings. First, have students cut out from magazines or newspapers pictures of people showing various feelings. Second, have them sort the pictures into the four feelings groups. (It may be difficult for students to differentiate or identify some expressions, but encourage them to use their judgment. Another possibility is to make a fifth category for "other" feelings.) If this is a group activity, you may want to provide each group with four boxes for sorting the pictures. Third, direct the children to glue the pictures in the appropriate column on the poster.

   Discuss the completed posters. Ask students why they think the people feel sad, angry, afraid, or happy. If the class set aside questionable pictures, take time to talk about them. What expressions do students think they show? Tell the class that often other feelings go along with the main feelings, that we have many feelings besides the four main feelings. If time permits, elicit from students feelings that may go along with feeling happy (excited, contented, relaxed, friendly, proud) or feeling angry (unfriendly, unhappy, gloomy, lonely).

4. **Closure:** "Today we talked about four main feelings. There are times when we feel sad, afraid, angry, and happy. Of course, we can have many feelings besides these four main feelings. We can often tell how a person feels by the way he or she looks (refer to posters). We also learned that everyone feels happy, sad, afraid, or angry sometimes."

● ●

Related Activities

1. Play music with changing moods. Use selections such as *Peter and the Wolf* by Prokofiev, *Carnival of the Animals* by Saint-Saens, *Pictures at an Exhibition* by Moussorgsky, or *Scenes from Childhood* by Schumann.

2. Display examples of art expressing different moods or feelings. Encourage students to tell which pictures make them feel happy, sad, or afraid.

3. Make copies of the four feelings faces (in reduced size) for class members to cut out and paste in their journals. Then have them compose a few lines about each feeling.

4. Enjoy books and songs that tie in with the lesson. One excellent choice, *On Monday When It Rained* by Cherryl Kachenmeister, shows how a boy felt on each day of the week. See the Lesson Resources listing at the beginning of the unit for other suggestions.

LESSON 4: FEELING HAPPY, SAD, AND AFRAID

Preparation/Materials
- Health puppets
- Plan and practice the puppet script.
- Optional: write the poem "Sometimes" on chart paper.

Objectives
- Students will infer how others are feeling.
- Students will practice checking their guesses about others' feelings by asking.
- Students will understand that there are various ways of dealing with emotions.

Background
Some people are more emotionally expressive than others. Children will also differ in expressiveness, but typically they are not burdened with as many inhibitions as adults, and therefore they feel freer to express their emotions. However, older children or adults who are uncomfortable with open expressions of fear or sadness may squelch this freedom, admonishing young children not to cry ("Big boys/girls don't cry") or not to be afraid ("Scaredy cat!"). In this lesson stress that when something sad happens, it's fitting to cry and that when something scary happens, it's okay to be afraid.

• •

Lesson

1. Start off with the puppets acting out a happy situation, such as going on a picnic.

   Script starter:
   > Sam: I'm glad your family said you could come along. We're going to have fun. My dad said that at this zoo we can feed some of the animals—the ducks and chickens and a goat and a pig.
   > Terry: Can we ride on the ponies, too?
   > Sam: Sure. That's the best part. The last time I rode on a black pony that went fast. We were almost galloping.

   Continue the happy mood of the dialogue. Ask students how they think the puppets are feeling and then ask the puppets to confirm their guess. ("Terry and Sam, we think that you're feeling happy. Did we guess right?") Have puppets tell how they're feeling and why.

2. Then use the puppets to act out the emotion of sadness or disappointment. Continue the story: Terry and Sam are disappointed because the pony stable is closed when they finally get to that part of the zoo.

   > Terry: This is lots of fun. I liked feeding the goat the best. I thought she was going to butt me in the stomach, but she didn't.
   > Sam: Now let's go ride the ponies.
   > Terry: I'm glad we saved the best for last.

Sam: Oh, oh, Terry. There's no one at the pony stable.

Terry: Oh no! We're too late. The stable's closed.

Again, interrupt the dialogue and have students guess and then ask the puppets how they are feeling.

3. Continue the puppet dialogue. This time act out the emotion of fear. Have Terry become frightened when Sam hides.

   Sam: C'mon. Let's explore the rest of the zoo.

   Terry: Wow! Look at that bird with the bright feathers and the long tail!

   Sam: I like the monkeys the best.

   Terry: So do I. (While Terry is engrossed in watching the monkeys, Sam runs and hides. Put Sam behind a book or behind a desk.)

   Look at that little monkey hanging on to its mother. Even when she makes a big jump he doesn't fall of. Look, Sam … Sam? (Show Terry becoming frightened when he can't find Sam.)

Interrupt the dialogue and ask students to describe how Terry is feeling and why. Then finish the dialogue, resolving the situation.

4. **Circle talk.** Give students opportunity to talk about what makes them happy, sad, or afraid. Perhaps refer to the lists of the previous lesson and add to them. Make the point that sometimes it's fitting to feel sad, for example, when we've done something wrong. But telling someone and saying we're sorry helps. Stress the comfort of knowing that God loves us and cares about us when we're sad or afraid and that we can talk to God about what is making us sad or afraid when we pray.

5. Read and talk about the following poem by Jack Prelutsky. If you have written the poem on chart paper, display the chart and read the poem from the chart.

   Sometimes
   Sometimes I simply have to cry,
   I don't know why,
   I don't know why.
   There's really nothing very wrong,
   I probably should sing a song
   or run around and make some noise
   or sit and tinker with my toys
   or pop a couple of balloons
   or play a game or watch cartoons,
   but I'm feeling sad,
   though I don't know why,
   and all I want to do is cry.

Pay particular attention to the "I don't know why" line. Make the point that although our feelings are influenced by situations (as in the puppet dialogue), at times we're simply in a sad or mean mood—and don't know why.

6. **Student activity.** Have students in pairs or small groups act out the story of Sam and Terry going to the zoo or other situations discussed during class.

7. **Closure:** "Today we talked about feeling happy and sad and afraid. Like Sam and Terry, our feelings don't stay the same. What can we do to feel better when we're feeling sad or afraid?"

● ●

Related Activities

1. Read books that tie in to the lesson. Suggested titles: Elspeth Murphy's *Sometimes I Think "What If?" Psalm 46 for Children, Sometimes Everything Feels Just Right: Psalm 104 for Children,* or *Sometimes I Have to Cry: Verses From the Psalms on Tears; Love You Forever* by Robert Munsch; *Sometimes I Worry …* by Alan Gross; *Jim's Dog Muffins* by Miriam Cohen; *I Am Not a Crybaby* by Norma Simon. (See Lesson Resources for complete list.)

2. Sing "He's Got the Whole World in His Hands" (*Psalter Hymnal*, 457; *Songs of God's Love*, 56), "Children of the Heavenly Father" (*Songs of God's Love*, 62; *Psalter Hymnal*, 440), or "Thank You for Giving Me the Morning" (*Proclaim Songbook 2*, 21).

3. Integrate with language arts by writing a class story about something that has happened since the beginning of the school year to make the class happy or sad.

4. Class members can illustrate the poem "Sometimes." Use the illustrations to create a booklet for students to read in the book center. Consider making an audio recording of the poem for them to listen to as they look at the book.

LESSON 5: FEELING ANGRY

Preparation/Materials
- Plan a scene depicting anger.
- Drawing or construction paper (white or manila), one sheet per student
- Optional: props for acting out scene

Objectives
- Students will identify situations that lead to anger.
- Students will check their guesses about others' feelings by asking.
- Students will identify specific ways of dealing with anger.

Background
Anger is a disturbing emotion. It's so disturbing that we tend to think of it as purely negative and destructive. But anger has a positive side. Anger over unjust treatment, for example, can become a catalyst for change. Anger can move us to confront prejudice or demand justice. We know, however, that unbridled expression of anger, with no attempt at resolution, breeds more anger. And the Bible specifically warns about the destructiveness of runaway anger. We know, too, that repressed or unresolved anger simmering within can lead to actual physical illness.

As you teach this lesson, help students begin to identify healthy and responsible ways of expressing anger and ways to defuse situations that may lead to anger.

Lesson
1. Refer to the poster of the angry face. Ask: "How do you feel when you're angry?" Identify other feelings that are closely related to anger, such as being upset or frustrated.

2. Act out a scene about anger for the class. Tell students that in the last lesson they saw Sam and Terry act out a story about going to the zoo, but this time you will do the acting and they can ask you questions.

Introduce yourself as a first grader named Christie or Chris. Look angry and describe a problem that has made you angry. For example: "I'm never going to help Jamie again! And even if he asks me, I'm not going to play with him either."

Interrupt your monologue to encourage class members to identify your feeling and to ask why you're feeling the way you are. Answer their questions and describe the situation or problem. (For example, after you helped Jamie build a garage, parking lot, and store with blocks, Jamie asked someone else to play cars with him. Or after you found a lost ball for Jamie, he ran off to play ball with others.)

Pose the problem of what to do next. ("Well, what can I do now?") Ask the class for possible solutions to the problem and then have them choose what to do.

Act out the class's solution and show a pleased facial expression when you work things out.

3. Ask the class for suggestions of another situation that might make them feel angry. Act the situation out with a student, or have the students fill both roles. Have the class come up with responsible ways to deal with the anger or frustration. Allow them to do some creative problem solving and choose which solution they think is best. Possible situations: a friend takes personal items without asking, a classmate teases or bullies, a teacher or parent interrupts a favorite activity such as reading or watching TV.

4. **Circle talk.** Brainstorm ways to ways to deal with anger. Include the following ideas:
   - Don't do anything right away. Calm down first so that you won't do anything you will be sorry for. Perhaps try counting slowly from 1-10.
   - Talk with the person who made you angry. Tell him or her how you feel and why. Then listen to what the other person has to say. Try to work it out.
   - Do something to work off your anger. Read a favorite book or take a drink of water or get back to work.

   Clearly make the point that everybody gets angry and that's not bad, but being angry doesn't mean we can hurt others.

5. **Student activity.** Give the class a sentence starter—"I get angry when …" Have the students complete the sentence and draw a picture of something that makes them angry. Ask students to show their drawings to the class and together talk about ways of dealing with the situation.

6. **Closure:** "We talked about feeling angry today. We all get angry sometimes, don't we? Because we're upset when we're angry, sometimes we do things we're sorry for later. What are some things that can help us when we're angry?" (Refer to list in step 4.)

• •

Related Activities

1. Read and discuss a story about someone who became angry. Suggested titles: *The Quarreling Book* by Charlotte Zolotow, *We Are Best Friends* by Aliki, *Martha's Mad Day* by Miranda Hapgood, *Sometimes I Get Mad: Psalm 73 for Children* by Elspeth Murphy, *Let's Be Enemies* by Janice May Udry. Consider having the class make up an alternative ending to the story or suggest an alternative way to deal with the problem presented in the story.

2. Center idea: have students make finger-paintings expressing how they feel when they're angry.

3. Center idea: pairs or groups of students can use classroom puppets or other manipulatives to act out the situations and the resolutions covered during the whole group session.

4. Poems to enjoy: "The Wrong Start" by Marchette Chute, "Sulk" and "They're Calling" by Felice Holman (both in *The Random House Book of Poetry for Children*).

LESSON 6: HOW DO YOU FEEL?

Preparation/Materials
- Book to read aloud about feelings
- Posters of feelings and lists of situations/feelings

Objectives
- Students will identify ways to respond to others' feelings.
- Students will develop empathy.

Background

Only as children mature both intellectually and emotionally can they begin to see a situation from another's point of view. "One way," says Mary Vander Goot, "to encourage children to take social responsibility for their own actions is to teach them to identify the consequences of their emotional expressions on others." Encour-aging empathy is the best way to help students learn to be considerate of each other in the classroom. Sometimes this may involve placing students in a situation where they experience the same feelings that they inflicted on others. For example, a child who loves to tease may not understand how the victim feels until the teacher allows the victim to give the teaser a taste of teasing. "Child-centered outcomes," concludes Vander Goot, "are probably more ef-fective than teacher-centered rules."

In the preceding lessons students have learned to identify the connection of feelings to body language and the situations that may lead to certain feelings. In this lesson the focus is on how we can help others when we know they're sad, unhappy, or angry.

• •

Lesson

1. Begin by reading a story that deals with feelings. A few suggested titles: *Ira Says Goodbye* by Bernard Waber, *We Are Best Friends* by Aliki, *What's the Matter With Carruthers?* by James Marshall, *Whistle for Willie* by Ezra Keats, *Mary, Mary* by Sarah Hayes, and *What's Wrong, Tom?* by Emma and Paul Rogers.

2. Discuss the story, stressing the feelings of the main character. Ask students to close their eyes and pretend to be the main character. Ask: "If you were (name), how would you have felt when (describe an incident from the story)?" Then have students identify what others in the story did to make the main character feel better or perhaps tell what they would have done if they would have been the character's friend.

3. Teach students the song "We Love" by Ann Price. After they learn the words, have them add clapping. Use the song as a basis for discussing why we love others. Teach the class God's commandment: "Love God above all and others (your neighbor) as your-self."

4. **Closure:** "Today we talked about caring about others' feelings, about loving others." Ask students to recite God's commandment.

5. Use the posters of feelings and students' lists of situations in which those feelings commonly occur to review unit concepts.

Related Activities

*   Show the video *Pine Tree Club*. This resource can be used to review many unit concepts.

Unit 2

Created to Live in a Family

Goals

- Students will recognize God's design for the continuation of life.
- Students will develop their understanding of family life—its purpose, responsibilities, and common changes.
- Students will understand the life cycle.
- Students will develop a Christian perspective on death.

Background

God created us to live in relationship with others. Genesis 2 pictures God the Creator thinking over Adam's relationships and deciding that Adam needed another human being with whom to share his life. "It is not good for the man to be alone. I will make a helper suitable for him" (verse 18). Marriage and, by extension, the family are part of a loving God's plan for human life. The Scriptures affirm this throughout (see, for example, Psalm 127: 3-4). The idea that marriage is a good gift is highlighted by the frequent use in Scripture of marriage as a metaphor of God's relationship to his people (Hosea 1-4, Isaiah 54:4-6, Mark 2:19-20, Ephesians 5:22-33, Revelation 19:7-9).

But marriage and family life have not escaped the effects of sin. Because we are sinful, we have no power within ourselves to maintain healthy family relationships. Our brokenness is reflected in family life. But in Christ we can find healing, forgiveness, and the power to restore relationships and make new beginnings.

With this Christian perspective in mind, how do we teach a unit on the family? As Christians we want to celebrate the joy of God's good gift of family, but we also must recognize the existence of common family struggles. Our homes are not trouble free, and glossing over the effects of sin is not helpful to our students. The Bible is brutally honest in its picture of family life. Think of the stories about the families of Jacob, David, and Solomon. Teaching the unit in a moralistic way will only serve to make students who live in troubled families feel guilty. God is present in both troubled and tranquil families. The good news is that God came to sinners, to all those with broken and contrite hearts.

Vocabulary

Integrate the following suggested vocabulary:

living	babies	mother	church	grandfather
nonliving	kinds	father	people	grandmother
plants	cousin	change	brother	praise
animals	aunt	death	sister	group
seeds	uncle	worship	serve	home
eggs	home	love	family	change

Unit Resources

Anderson, Ray S., and Dennis B. Guernsey. *On Being Family: A Social Theology of the Family.*

Grand Rapids: Eerdmans, 1985.

Written by two Fuller Seminary professors, the book's central thesis is that "God has placed human persons in a created order for which the covenant love of God provides the fundamental paradigm" for the formation of family life.

Canadian Families: Media Kit. Kanata Series (redeveloped). Weigl Educational Publishers, 1984.

The kit features five Canadian families of various ethnic roots: Jamaican, Ukrainian, Japanese, Native, and French Canadian. Students learn about similarities and differences in the ways the families live. The kit includes posters, an audiocassette, and a teacher guide.

Greene, Carol. *Why Boys and Girls Are Different.* Learning About Sex Series. St. Louis: Concordia, 1982.

Written from a solid Christian perspective for ages 3-5, the book covers differences between boys and girls (uses the words *vagina* and *penis*). It also talks about different kinds of families and places the Christian family within the context of God's family. An excellent resource for this unit; however, the art gives the impression of embarrassment with the subject (everyone has large eyes and sheepish expressions).

Hoberman, Mary Ann. *Fathers, Mothers, Sisters, Brothers: A Collection of Family Poems.* Boston: Little, Brown, 1991.

Humorous and serious poems celebrating every kind of family member.

Hart, Carole, and others, eds. *Free to Be … You and Me.* Toronto/New York: Bantam, 1972.

A collection of poems, stories, and songs that attempt to break down stereotypes and promote self-esteem.

My Family and Me. Media kit. Encyclopedia Brittanica, 1981.

The kit consists of four filmstrips with accompanying audiocassetes entitled What Is a Family? How Do We Help Each Other? What Are Family Rules? and How Do Families Change? A teacher guide contains a summary of the content, questions for discussion, and suggestions for student activities.

Lesson Resources

Lesson 2

Babies of the Home. Videocassette. Available from Kimbo.

Shows small puppies, kittens with eyes still closed, and a tiny parakeet pecking its way out of the egg. For ages 3-10. Running time of 45 minutes.

Barnyard Babies. Videocassette. Available from Kimbo.

Shows babies taking their first steps and mothers cleaning, feeding, and caring for their babies. For ages 3-10. Running time of 45 minutes.

Brown, Margaret W. *Baby Animals.* Reprint of 1941 edition. New York: Random, 1989.

Carle, Eric. *The Tiny Seed.* Saxonville, Mass.: Picture Book Studio, 1987.

Fisher, Aileen. *Listen, Rabbit.* New York: Crowell, 1964.

Freedman, Russell. *Farm Babies.* New York: Holiday, 1981.

Heller, Ruth. *Animals Born Alive and Well.* New York: Grosset and Dunlap, 1982.

_____. *Chickens Aren't the Only Ones.* A Reading Rainbow Book. New York: Grosset and Dunlap, 1981.

Merriam, Eve. *Boys & Girls, Girls & Boys.* New York: Holt, 1972.

Penny, Malcolm. *Animals and Their Young.* Animal Kingdom Series. New York: Watts, 1987.
    Intended for grades 1-6.

Selsam, Millicent. *All Kinds of Babies.* New York: Harper, 1963.

_____. *Egg to Chick.* Revised edition. New York: HarperCollins, 1987.

Lessons 3 and 4

Billy's World. Native Education Series. Reidmore Books, 1989.
    Set in the Northlands of Alberta, this story tells of a boy who goes on a trip with his grandfather and finds peace and a sense of completeness in the bush.

Dantzer-Rosenthal, Marya. *Some Things Are Different, Some Things Are the Same.* Niles, Ill., Whitman, 1986.
    Compares the homes and families of two friends.

Goffstein, Marilyn. *Family Scrapbook.* New York: Farrar, Straus & Giroux, 1978.

Hoberman, Mary Ann. *A House Is a House for Me.* New York: Viking, 1978.

Rosen, Michael. *We're Going on a Bear Hunt.* New York: McElderry, 1989.

Simon, Norma. *All Kinds of Families.* Niles, Ill.: Whitman, 1975.

Vendrell, Carme, and J.M. Parramón. *Family: Parents.* Educational Series. Toronto/New York: Barron's, 1987.
    About the role of parents in raising and caring for children and about how feelings of a child can affect a parent.

_____. *Family: Grandparents.* Educational Series. Toronto/New York: Barron's, 1987.
    About the place of grandparents in the family.

Williams, Vera. *A Choice for My Mother.* New York: Greenwillow, 1982.

Lesson 5

Blaine, Marge. *The Terrible Thing That Happened at Our House.* Reprint of 1975 edition. New York: Four Winds, 1984.

Changing Homes. Canadian Family Series. Post Mills, Vt.: Chelsea Green/Fitzhenry and Whiteside, 1986.
    Three children—Gretchen, Sandy, and Joey—from two different families learn to live together as a family when their parents get married.

Henkes, Kevin. *Julius: Baby of the World.* New York: Greenwillow, 1990.

Hoban, Russell. *A Baby Sister for Frances.* New York: Harper, 1964.

Keats, Ezra. *Peter's Chair.* New York: Harper, 1967.

Lesson 6

Brown, Margaret Wise. *The Dead Bird.* Reprint of 1958 edition. New York: HarperCollins, 1989.

Cohen, Miriam. *Jim's Dog Muffins.* New York: Greenwillow, 1984.

Keller, Holly. *Goodbye, Max.* New York: Greenwillow, 1984.

Kopp Ruth. *Where Has Grandpa Gone?* Grand Rapids: Zondervan, 1983.
> Written from a Christian perspective, this teacher resource describes how a child perceives death at various age levels and gives suggestions for guiding children through times of loss. Includes a read-aloud section to help explain the meaning of death to children.

Sanford, Doris. *It Must Hurt a Lot: A Child's Book About Death.* Portland, Ore.: Multnomah, 1986.

Stock, Catherine. *Better With Two.* New York: Harper, 1988.

Wahl, Mats. *Grandfather's Laika.* Minneapolis: Carolrhoda Books, 1990
> A grandfather and grandson work through their grief together when Laika, a much-loved golden retriever, becomes sick and dies.

Lesson 7
The following is a list of student resources (K-2):

Books dealing with moving and change or loss

Aliki. *We Are Best Friends.* New York: Greenwillow, 1982.

Hickman, Martha. *My Friend William Moved Away.* Nashville: Abingdon, 1979.

Hughes, Shirley. *Moving Molly.* New York: Lothrop, 1988.

Sharmat, Marjorie. *Mitchell Is Moving.* Reading Rainbow Book. New York: Macmillan, 1978.

Waber, Bernard. *Ira Says Goodbye.* Boston: Houghton, 1988.

Zolotow, Charlotte. *Janey.* New York: Harper, 1973.

Books dealing with human death

Clifton, Lucille. *Everett Anderson's Goodbye.* New York: Holt, 1983.
> Everett grieves for his dead father. The book begins with a list of the five stages of grieving and then follows Everett through each stage of grief.

dePaola, Tomie. *Nana Upstairs, Nana Downstairs.* New York: Puffin, 1973.

Egger, Bettina. *Marianne's Grandmother.* New York: Dutton, 1987.

Gould, Deborah. *Grandpa's Slide Show.* New York: Lothrop, 1987.

Kaldhol, Marit, and Wenche Oyen. *Goodbye Rune.* New York: Kane/Miller, 1987.

Cohn, Janice. *I Had a Friend Named Peter: Talking to Children About Death.* New York: Morrow, 1987.

LESSON 1: LIVING AND NONLIVING THINGS

Preparation/Materials

- Picture(s) showing living and nonliving things. Include pictures of plants, animals, and people.
- Student Activity page

Objectives

- Students will distinguish between living and nonliving things.
- Students will classify three kinds of living things: plants, animals, and human beings.

Lesson

1. Briefly review the concept of alike/different taught in Lesson 2 of Unit 1. Tell students that one way people are all alike is that they are alive.

2. Display the pictures and have students identify the living and nonliving things depicted. Teach *living* and *nonliving* as new vocabulary. Elicit from students that living things move and grow and that nonliving things don't. (A later lesson discusses what living things need to grow.)

   Have students study the pictures of living things carefully. Lead students to identify three kinds of living things: plants, animals, and people. Teach new vocabulary. Together classify the pictures. Then have students decide which category they belong in.

3. **Student activity.** Have students complete the activity page, drawing a blue circle around the pictures of things that are alive and a red circle around the pictures of things that are not alive. As you discuss the pictures, talk about how the living things are alike (they move and grow). Lead students to understand that God gives life and sustains it.

4. **Closure.** Ask questions such as the following:
   - "What is the main difference between living and nonliving things?"
   - "Name a nonliving thing."
   - "Name a living thing."
   - "What are you—living or nonliving?"
   - "Who gives you life?"

Related Activities

1. At a center make mobiles of pictures of living things. Have students draw the pictures or cut them out of magazines. Direct class members to mount the pictures on construction paper and then punch a hole in the top of each. Use yarn to hang the pictures from a dowel or coat hanger.

2. Another center idea: provide sets of pictures of living and nonliving things and/or of plants, animals, and people for students to classify.

LESSON 2: LIVING THINGS REPRODUCE

Preparation/Materials
- Student Activity pages or picture illustrating living/nonliving things from previous lesson
- A few seeds and an egg
- Pictures depicting living things and their young: plants and seeds; birds, poultry, or reptiles and their eggs; cats, dogs, cows, and their young; human parents and baby
- Student Activities 1 & 2
- Optional but highly recommended: seeds to plant, soil, and containers; a hamster, gerbil, or another small animal and its young to observe over a period of time in the classroom; or eggs to hatch

Objectives
- Students will understand that living things reproduce themselves through eggs or seeds.
- Students will be aware that human beings grow inside a mother's body and are born alive.
- Students will be aware that God planned for the continuation of life in this way.

Background
The concept of reproduction may be totally new to many students. Teach the lesson in a way that communicates that reproduction is a normal part of life. Children at this age are often curious about animal reproduction and the interaction of animal parents with their young, so this is a good age at which introduce the basic facts of reproduction. Be prepared to answer students' questions in an honest, straightforward way. But beyond that use this lesson as an opportunity to instill wonder at God's intricate plan for the continuation of life.

Lesson
1. Use a visual or a copy of the Student Activity pictures of the previous lesson to review the concept of living and nonliving.

2. Show students the seeds and eggs. Explain that this is the way living things start. Plants start as little seeds, and then sprout and grow; other living things start as eggs.

3. Display the pictures of plants and seeds and of animals and humans and their young. Explain that some animals grow in eggs outside of the mother's body. Describe how birds or chickens keep the eggs warm in a nest until the little ones peck their way out. Then tell students that some living things are born alive from their mothers. Kittens, puppies, and human babies are all born this last way. These mothers keep the babies warm inside of them until it is time to be born. Emphasize that God planned for life to continue on earth in this way.

4. Teach the song "Animal Families." Contrast human families and animal families.

5. Start a class project on reproduction. Plant the seeds, get acquainted with the animal and its young, and/or explain the egg-hatching procedure.

6. **Student activity.** Have students cut out pictures of the young and paste them in the correct "parent picture." Go over the completed activity with the class. Ask whether the things pictured are living or nonliving. Have class members identify which of the young pictured grow inside the mother's body and which are from eggs outside of the mother's body.

7. **Closure:** "Today we talked about living things. God's plan for this world includes a way for new living things to start or to be born." (Elicit from class members the way living things start.)

● ●

Related Activities

1. Read books on the lesson topic. Some suggested titles:
   Baby Animals by Margaret Wise Brown
   Farm Babies by Russell Freedman
   Animals and Their Young by Malcolm Penny
   The Tiny Seed by Eric Carle
   Listen, Rabbit by Aileen Fisher
   All Kinds of Babies and *Egg to Chick* by Millicent Selsam

   Chickens Aren't the Only Ones and *Animals Born Alive and Well* by Ruth Heller.

2. Make a class booklet illustrating the song "Animal Families" and an audio recording of the class singing the song. Put the booklet and recording at a center for students to enjoy.

Animal Families

L.,H.B.

Lois and Herb Brokering

The tur - tle's home is on his back. He does - n't know his
The ba - by cat is on short and fat. He sucks milk from his
The but - ter - fly will lay an egg. Out comes a cat - er -
Some - one to love and take good care is what God planned for

moth - er._____ He eats what - ev - er comes a - long and
moth - er._____ She cleans him with her rough, pink tongue, and
pil - lar._____ She eats some leaves, then eats some more. It
me._____ Moth - er, fath - er, aunt, or grand - ma.

then he eats an - oth - er._____ That's the way God made him.
then she cleans his broth - er._____ That's the way God made her.
takes a lot to fill her!_____ That's the way God made me.
Guess who it can be?_____ That's the way God made me.

That's the way God made him. That's the way God made him, but
That's the way God made her. That's the way God made her, but
That's the way God made me. That's the way God made me, that's

he is not like me.
she is not like me.
how I like to be.

LESSON 3: LIVING IN FAMILIES

Preparation/Materials

- For student booklets:
  drawing paper
  art materials
- Optional: write the poem on chart paper.

Objectives

- Students will recognize that God's plan for humans includes living in families.
- Students will identify their parents' responsibility to love and care for them, but also to discipline them.

Background

"God established marriage and, by extension, the family as a cornerstone of creation," says *Horizons Health's* statement of philosophy. This lesson teaches students that families are part of God's loving design for the human race and makes them aware of the blessings of family life.

However, in this lesson students will talk not only about the warmth of family life but also touch on its tensions and frictions. People of all ages experience swings in mood from day to day. It is important that students learn that relationships with others, especially with family members, can affect their feelings. Also they need to learn that they can affect the feelings of their family members—that is, the ways in which they interact with other family members can affect the moods of their siblings and parents. Children need reassurance that family friction does not mean that family members don't love each other. And they need to know that in Christ they can find healing for broken relationships and hurts, forgiveness, and the power to make new beginnings. By relying on God's grace and asking for the Spirit's power, families can experience joy.

• •

Lesson

1. Begin by reading the following poem about home by Jack Prelutsky. If you have written the poem on chart paper, display and read from the chart.

> **Home! You're Where It's Warm Inside**
> Home! You are a special place;
> you're where I wake and wash my face,
> brush my teeth and comb my hair,
> change my socks and underwear,
> clean my ears and blow my nose,
> try on all my parents' clothes.
>
> Home! You're where it's warm inside,
> where my tears are gently dried,
> where I'm comforted and fed,
> where I'm forced to go to bed,
> where there's always love to spare;
> Home! I'm glad that you are there.

2. Discuss the poem. Emphasize that living in families is God's plan for us. Ask students why this is necessary. (The adults in the family provide for the children.)

   Lead students to identify ways their parents care for them (love, feed, and clothe them; provide shelter; take care of them when they're sick; help them in many ways; teach them about serving God). Make an experience chart with the class or list on the board ways parents provide.

   Use the poem line "where I'm forced to go to bed" to comment on discipline and obedience as a necessary part of family life. And refer to the line "where my tears are gently dried" to point out that sometimes we are unhappy at home, too. Sometimes family members may hurt their feelings or they may do or say something that upsets others. Talk about forgiveness and new beginnings in family life.

   Tell students that although parents are important in families, so are children. Children can help their parents, and in families with more than one child, children can also help each other.

   Identify things that families do together such as working, talking, eating, and playing. Christian families also pray, read the Bible, and praise God together. (The following lesson will identify specific things children can do to help in their families.)

3. Have students illustrate the poem "Home! You're Where It's Warm Inside." Consider making a class booklet about the poem and dividing the lines to be illustrated among the students. (Suggestion: make the book in the shape of a house.) If the class is large, assign several students to illustrate each line. Write the line on the bottom of the first of the illustrations. As you read the completed book with the class, have class members identify which of the basic needs the poem refers to. Which of the needs is not mentioned in the poem?

   Keep the completed book in the book center for students to read. If the book will receive hard use, you may wish to have the pages laminated.

4. **Closure:** "God planned for people to live in families. Why is that a good plan?" (Refer students to the experience chart.)

Related Activities

1. Read *A House Is a House for Me* by Mary Ann Hoberman. Have children write poems, patterning their poems after the text of the book.

2. Journal idea: Give the children some open-ended sentences to complete in their journals (for example, "I like it when my family …"; "I don't like it when my family …"; "Something special about my family is …"; "It makes me mad when my (brother/sister/parent …").

3. Enjoy a family feast. Invite the families of your students to a potluck celebrating the family. Send a note home asking each family to bring a favorite dish to share. Encourage parents to have the child help with reading the recipe, measuring, and mixing. Allow each student the opportunity to introduce his or her family to the rest of the class. Take pictures at the dinner, and make them into a class book.

LESSON 4: ALL KINDS OF FAMILIES

Preparation/Materials
- Story or poem about family life to read aloud
- Pictures of family members doing various common family jobs
- Student Activity page

Objectives
- Students will be able to describe how families are alike and different.
- Students will describe ways in which they can contribute to family life.
- Students will choose to help their families in specific ways.

Background
Discussing families and family groupings can be very painful for students whose families do not fit the pattern of two parents and one or more children living together. In teaching this lesson be sensitive to the variety of family groupings represented in the class. This is an excellent opportunity to model loving acceptance of differences.

• •

Lesson

1. Read a story to the class about family life. Suggested titles: *All Kinds of Families* by Norma Simon, *Family Scrapbook* by Marilyn Goffstein, and *We're Going on a Bear Hunt* retold by Michael Rosen.

2. Use the story or poem as a starting point for discussing how families are alike and different. Or enjoy a poem from the collection *Fathers, Mothers, Sisters, Brothers* by Mary Ann Hoberman. Questions such as the following will help stimulate discussion:
   - "What does your family do that's the same as (the character's) family?"
   - "What does your family do that (the character's) family doesn't do?"
   - "Does your family have more or less people in it?"
   - "Name one way your family is like all other families."
   Make clear that families can be made up of various groupings of people.

3. Have the class identify "family" words, names showing family relationships. Include extended family—cousins, aunt, uncle, grandmother, and grandfather. Perhaps list the words on the board. Then use the family words in the following song called "Cousin Peter." Begin by teaching and singing the first verse.

   Sing this second verse:

   > He hung his hat upon a peg.
   > He hung his hat upon a peg.
   > He hung his hat upon a peg
   > To show that he was here.

   Add verses to describe other things Cousin Peter did while he was visiting, and have students mime the actions:

He wiped his shoes upon the mat, etc.
He kicked his shoes off one by one, etc.
He danced about in his stocking feet, etc.
He played he was a great big bear, etc.
He tossed us up into the air, etc.
He made a bow and said goodbye, etc.

Make up more verses about other relations coming to visit—Aunt Matilda, Uncle Matthew, Cousin Martha, Grandma Fisher, Grandpa Cosby.

4. Explain that in a family all members are important and contribute to family life. Show the class pictures of parents and children doing a variety of family jobs. Ask students to describe what's going on in each picture. Why does each of these jobs need to be done in a family? Have volunteers tell how these jobs are done in their family. Make the point that different families handle things differently.

5. **Student activity.** Use the activity sheet to discuss ways students can help their families. Then ask students to color and cut out the coupons. Staple the the coupons together to make booklets for students to take home and give to parents. Periodically, ask students how they have helped at home.

6. **Closure:** "Today we learned more about living in families. We talked about ways families can be alike and different. And we talked about jobs that need to be done in a home. We can all help to get the work done."

• •

Related Activities

1. Center idea: have students work in groups or pairs to make collages of families. Share the collages and ask students to identify ways in which the families are alike and different.

2. Each class member can make a booklet about his or her family. Include a family portrait and picture of the family's favorite activities.

3. Small groups of students can act out family scenes, showing what happens in the home on a weekday morning, at dinner, during a typical evening, and on Sunday morning.

4. Send a note home asking parents to help their child write a few sentences about a special tradition their family has. The child may draw a picture to illustrate. For show and tell have the children "read" or tell about their family tradition. Compare simi-

larities and differences. Then put all the sheets into a class book.

5. Have each child bring in a picture of their family to show. Discuss how the families are alike and different. Put all the pictures on a bulletin board display under the heading "The Family of God." (For Lesson 8 add a border using magazine pictures of families from around the world.) Integrate with math by graphing the number in each family.

6. This is also a good time to talk about the differently abled in families. Read a book such as *I Have a Sister, My Sister Is Deaf* by J. Peterson or *My Sister Kate: How She Sees God's World* by Christine Wright. Look into having "Kids on the Block," a group of differently abled puppets, give a presentation in your classroom or school.

Cousin Peter

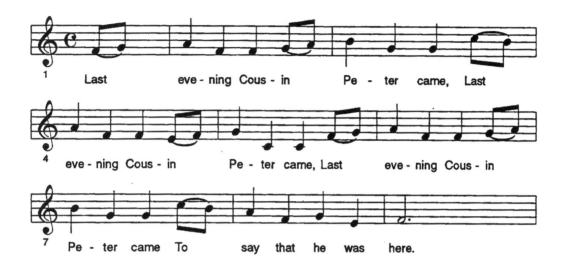

Sing this second verse:

> He hung his hat upon a peg.
> He hung his hat upon a peg.
> He hung his hat upon a peg
> To show that he was here.

Add verses to describe other things Cousin Peter did while he was visiting, and have students mime the actions:

> He wiped his shoes upon the mat, etc.
> He kicked his shoes off one by one, etc.
> He danced about in his stocking feet, etc.
> He played he was a great big bear, etc.
> He tossed us up into the air, etc.
> He made a bow and said goodbye, etc.

Make up more verses about other relations coming to visit—Aunt Matilda, Uncle Matthew, Cousin Martha, Grandma Fisher, Grandpa Cosby.

LESSON 5: CHANGE AND FAMILIES

Preparation/Materials

- Personal photographs or other pictures depicting change in a family
- Story about changes taking place in a family to read to the class
- Student Activity Sheets 1 & 2

Objectives

- Students will identify various ways in which families change.
- Students will describe changes in specific family groupings.

Background

Families change in expected ways: new children are born or adopted into families; children grow up, get married, and have children of their own; parents and grandparents grow older. There are also more painful ways in which families change, for example, through divorce and death. We tend to talk around or ignore the painful changes, but some young children must deal with them, and they need the support of the Christian community. Treating these topics as taboo only adds to the difficulty of the situation. Recognizing divorce as a kind of change that takes place in some families does not imply approval of divorce; it does take into account the reality of divorce in North American society and in the Christian community.

• •

Lesson

1. Introduce the concept of change in family groupings by showing the class several photographs that depict how your family has changed over the years. Have students identify the changes in the family and the possible reasons for them. (A number of explanations are possible: birth or adoption, growth, death or divorce.)

2. Discuss common ways in which families change: adding new children, older children getting married, grandparents coming to live, divorce, or death of family member. Again, it is important to be sensitive to classroom family situations.

3. Read a story dealing with change in family life. Suggested titles: *Peter's Chair* by Ezra Keats, *A Baby Sister for Frances* by Russell Hoban, *The Terrible Thing That Happened at Our House* by Marge Blaine, and *Julius: Baby of the World* by Kevin Henkes.

4. **Circle talk.** Discuss the story. Ask students to describe what change took place in the family and how the main character reacted to the change. How was the change finally accepted?

5. **Student activity.** Have the students refer to Activity Sheet 1 in their workbooks. Ask them to look carefully at the pictures of families. Explain or elicit from students that these are pictures of three different families. Note that the pictures cover a long period of time. Have the children identify the three family groups. If students have difficulty with this, they can use the framing pattern as a help.

Ask students to cut out the pictures and arrange one set of the pictures in sequence. Then have them study the pictures and describe how the family changed. Do the same thing with set 2 and 3. Encourage the class to explain possible reasons for the changes.

Family groupings:

Set 1—man and woman

man, woman, and child

man, woman, and two more children

Set 2—woman and child (possible reasons-death of husband or divorce)

woman, man, child (new marriage)

woman, man, and two children

Set 3—woman, man, and two children

same grouping, but older

another adult added (possibly grandparent)

Have students paste the family groups in the correct sequence on Activity Sheet 2.

6. **Closure.** Use the following questions to summarize and evaluate:
   - "What happens to all families?" (They change.)
   - "How did my family change?"
   - "What are some ways families change?"

• •

Related Activities

1. Journal idea: have the students write about a change that has happened in their family.

2. To facilitate further class discussion, have students build families using manipulatives. Provide a set of paper dolls or flannelgraph figures of family members (include a basic nuclear family, grandparents, and other adult figures). Display them in front of the class. Ask volunteers to take turns coming up to choose members to make a family. Then ask them to change the family in some way and to explain the reasons for their changes. (Idea adapted from *Teaching Young Children Using Themes* [Good Year, 1991].)

LESSON 6: THE LIFE CYCLE AND DEATH

Preparation/Materials
- Visual of living/nonliving things (from Lesson 1)
- Optional: dying plant or plant with dead flowers

Objectives
- Students will recognize that all living things grow, change, and die.
- Students will become aware that change and death cause feelings of sadness and loss.

Background

The tendency of many North American adults is to try to shield children from the reality of death. They wish to protect children, to keep the children's lives happy and carefree. But death is an inescapable part of life—even for children—in a world marred by sin. Trying to screen out death actually does children a disservice. In fact, with no guidance from parents or teachers, children may struggle with distorted ideas or fears. By guiding their learning about death, adults not only give children correct information, but also the possibility of sharing feelings and fears about death and, in the Christian community, the hope of resurrection life in Christ.

Ruth Kopp in a helpful book entitled *Where Has Grandpa Gone?* helps us understand the concept of death a child has at various age levels. Between the ages of two and six, most children see "everything that moves and has activity as being alive and personal." Since young children also tend to personify abstract ideas, as they become aware of death they think of it as a powerful being that can "come at will and remove people and pets" they love. They develop a variety of ways to fend off the "monster death." Children from about three and four years old, for example, may hide in the comfort of a security blanket, while from about four to six or seven, they use "fantasy, magic, and wishful thinking" to protect themselves and those they love. But gradually at about six or seven, children acquire what Kopp calls a materialist attitude toward death: they shift their protection against death "from fantasy to the tangible, physical world." In this phase they become aware of their bodies and how they work and find a defense against death in physical fitness—an idea reinforced by North American society. They think if they are strong and healthy enough, they can prevent illness or injury. During the next phase (from about eight to eleven), children rationally explore their world and the idea of death. They look for reasons and explanations for illnesses, for the most part ignoring the emotions.

So from a young age children are aware of death, and they struggle to deal with it. It isn't possible to shield them from death. However, by sensitively dealing with the subject, we can offer them support and hold out to them the comfort of being a child of God and trusting God to make all things well.

This lesson picks up on ideas presented earlier in the unit and builds on them to introduce the concept of death. The focus of this lesson is the death of plants and animals. (The next lesson deals with human death.) Bear in mind that although all the books suggested in step 3 deal with the death of pets, many of them do obliquely refer to the death of people. Also note that many of these books are not written from a Christian perspective, so it is crucial to read the books critically and to provide that perspective through comment and discussion.

Lesson

1. Review the concept of living and nonliving. Ask students to name some living and nonliving things. Ask: "How do we know when something is alive?" (It moves; it grows.)

2. Review the concept that living things grow and change. Refer to the classroom project, and have students identify how the plants and/or animals have grown and changed. Introduce the topic of death and the life cycle by noting parts of the plant that have died or by showing students a plant with dead parts. Tell students that living things grow, change, and also, finally, die.

3. **Circle talk.** Tell students about a pet you or one of your family members had that died or read one of the many excellent books available that approach the subject of death of a pet. Suggested book titles:

   Father's Laika by Mats Wahl
   Jim's Dog Muffins by Miriam Cohen
   Goodbye, Max by Holly Keller
   The Dead Bird by Margaret Wise Brown
   It Must Hurt a Lot: A Child's Book About Death by Doris Sanford
   Better With Two by Catherine Stock

   After reading the story, identify some of the feelings that the main character or characters had.

4. Allow time to discuss questions that students may pose or to give them opportunity to talk about family pets that have died.

5. **Closure.** Briefly summarize by reiterating that living things grow, change, and die.

LESSON 7: DEALING WITH DEATH

Preparation/Materials
* Books for Options 2 and 3

Objectives
* Students will recognize that all human beings must die.
* Students will recognize that in the face of death sadness is a fitting emotion.
* Students will identify/become aware of the Christian hope.

Background

This lesson on the death of human beings naturally follows the previous one; however, if you feel that Lesson 5 is sufficient introduction to the subject of death for your class at this time, use this lesson and its resources later in the school year when the subject comes up naturally in the classroom or fits in with the class's Bible studies (for example, tie it in with a lesson on the death of Moses or with your celebration of Easter).

Much of the current literature on death and dying presents death as the natural end of life. We are urged to accept death as natural and, sometimes, even as a beautiful and fitting end to life. It's true that in the world as we know it—a broken world suffering under the effects of sin—death is a fact, and the life cycle inevitably ends in death. But the Bible clearly teaches that death is not a friend, but an enemy. Death is the result of human sin. God created us not for death, but for life. Christians believe Christ has removed the sting of death, and in him we already have new life that never ends. Christ's resurrection body is the guarantee of the resurrection of our bodies.

The way you present this lesson will depend on what approach you are comfortable with and on your classroom situation. Thus this lesson provides several options and lists of resources from which to choose. Keep the lesson simple and present it in a matter-of-fact way. (A similar lesson and options are also included in the Horizons Health teacher guides for kindergarten and grade 2.)

Lesson

Option 1: Tell about the loss of someone you know, how sad you felt and how you missed the person. Talk about the source of your comfort and how that helped you.

Option 2: Begin by introducing the idea of loss by reading a book about moving and loss entailed by the person moving or staying. Use this as a starting point for discussing the loss of someone we know through death.
We Are Best Friends by Aliki
My Friend William Moved Away by Martha Hickman
Ira Says Goodbye by Bernard Waber
Janey by Charlotte Zolotow
Mitchell Is Moving by Marjorie Sharmat
Moving Molly by Shirley Hughes

Option 3: Read one of the books listed below. Although these books deal with death in a sensitive way, none of them is written from a Christian perspective. Thus it is important to read the books critically and spend time discussing the Christian hope in the face of death.

I Had a Friend Named Peter: Talking to Children About Death by Janice Cohn

Everett Anderson's Goodbye by Lucille Clifton

Marianne's Grandmother by Bettina Egger

Grandpa's Slide Show by Deborah Gould

Goodbye Rune by Marit Kaldhol and Wenche Oyen

Nana Upstairs, Nana Downstairs by Tomie dePaola

Option 4. Use an occasion that naturally arises in the classroom—the death of a relative or acquaintance of a class member—to talk about the subject of death. Be sure to stress the Christian hope, but also talk about feelings connected with death. Although Christians believe in new and eternal life in Christ, grief is nonetheless a fitting response to the loss of a loved one. Identify concrete ways to help the one who is grieving.

Use appropriate Scripture passages such as Psalm 23 or the story of Jesus' resurrection as a basis for continued discussion. And sing appropriate songs about Christ's resurrection or about the comfort of the Christian hope. A few suggested titles:

"Children of the Heavenly Father" (*Psalter Hymnal*, 440; *Songs of God's Love*, 62)

"He's Got the Whole World in His Hands" (*Songs of God's Love*, 56)

"The Lord's My Shepherd" (*Proclaim Songbook 2*, 16; *Psalter Hymnal*, 161; alternate tune, *Children's Hymnbook*, 19)

"Christ the Lord Is Risen Today" (*Proclaim Songbook 2*, 25)

LESSON 8: BELONGING TO THE FAMILY OF GOD

Preparation/Materials
- Chart paper
- Optional: additional songs of praise and/or songs about the family of God

Objectives
- Students will identify another family to which Christians belong: the family of God.
- Students will describe specific things the family of God does.
- Students will react by praising God for making them part of God's family.

Background
This lesson places the family within the context of the family of God. Christian parents and children are both, by adoption, children of God and part of the worldwide family of God. In this context, the family does not exist for its own sake. Rather, as Christians we offer our family life to God and live it in gratitude before God. The family, then, becomes a means of loving and serving God—and others.

Lesson

1. Tell students that in the last lessons the class has been talking about living and growing up in families. Explain that Christians also belong to another, bigger family. Lead students to identify that family as the family of God. Ask: "Who are in the family of God?" (All those who love and serve God—from all over the world.)

2. Work with the class to make an experience chart of activities of the family of God: worshiping and praising God, praying and studying the Bible, helping and loving each other, helping and loving others, telling others about Jesus, and so on. Illustrate the chart with sketches, illustrations, or photographs.

3. Thank God for including the families of the class in the family of God. Sing songs of praise to God and/or about the Church. Teach students the song based on verses of Psalm 100. Explain the meaning of "make a glad noise," "enter his gates," and "sheep of his pasture." Students will enjoy clapping and/or marching as they sing. Other suggested songs are: "The Church Is One Big Family" (*Proclaim Songbook 1*, 29), "Let Us Go to the House of the Lord" (*Proclaim Songbook 2*, 25), and "You Are Our God; We Are Your People" (*Psalter Hymnal*, 272).

4. **Closure:** "Today we learned that as Christians we are part of another family, the family of God. God's family is made up of people and of families from all over the world."

Related Activities

1. Focus on the diversity and wideness of the family of God by inviting international students or other visitors from overseas in your community to tell the class something about the family of God in their country.

2. Plan a service project in which students show love to other members of God's family. For example, the class can sing their favorite songs for a seniors' church group.

3. To increase students' world awareness, add to your bulletin board display of family pictures (Lesson 4) a border of magazine pictures of families from other countries and cultures.

Psalm 100

Based on Psalm 100:1,3,4   Czechoslovakian Folk Song

Unit 3

Living with Others

Goals

- Students will develop a Christian perspective on relationships with others.
- Students will develop skills for living in community.
- Students will choose to treat others with consideration.

Background

Christians recognize the power of sin to break down communication, mar relationships, and disrupt community. But Christians believe that the risen Christ has power to transform and renew us and our relationship to God and also to others. In this context "getting along with others" means much more than learning a set of skills (although interpersonal skills are important) or following a set of specific behavior patterns.

The apostle Paul addresses the problem of interpersonal relationships in these words: "But the fruit of the Spirit is love, joy, peace, patience, kindness, goodness, faithfulness, gentleness and self-control .... Since we live by the Spirit, let us keep in step with the Spirit. Let us not become conceited, provoking and envying each other" (Galatians 5: 22, 25, 26). Keeping in step with the Spirit will lead us away from self-centeredness—and toward the self-control and concern for others necessary for living in community.

This unit, then, is not a Dale Carnegie mini-course. The lessons are not meant to promote a self-serving "you scratch my back and I'll scratch yours" outlook. Rather, by giving students the opportunity to show courtesy, kindness, and love to others and to learn about getting along with others, we are nurturing them in the life of the Spirit.

Vocabulary

Integrate the following suggested vocabulary:

stop	sorry	problem	please
look	welcome	thank you	cooperate
listen	share	excuse me	manners

Unit Resources

Gibbs, Jeanne. *Tribes: A Process for Social Development and Cooperative Learning.* Santa Rosa, Calif.: Center Source Publications, 1987.

> Although the scope of this book is much broader than the content of this unit, its suggestions for cooperative activities make it a helpful teacher resource. Order from the publisher: 305 Tesconi Circle, Santa Rosa, California 95401.

Hill, Susan and Tim. *The Collaborative Classroom: A Guide to Co-operative Learning.* Portsmouth, N.H.: Heinemann, 1990.

> This book is "about people learning and working together, rather than alone." A valuable resource, not only for unit activities but also for establishing a truly cooperative classroom.

Hiller, Ron. *Ronno's "Getting Along" Theme Pack.* Kitchener, Ont.: Song Support, 1991.

> Includes "Let's Co-operate" and "The Good Manners Song," two original songs tying in with the unit theme. In the pack are a 38-page booklet with the piano/vocal score and an audio-

cassette. Order from the publisher: Station C, Box 722, Kitchener, Ontario, Canada N2G 4B6 or Suite 162, 255 Great Arrow Ave., Buffalo, New York 14207-3081.

Prutzman, Priscilla, and others. *Friendly Classroom for a Small Planet: A Handbook on Creative Approaches to Living and Problem Solving for Children.* Philadelphia: New Society Publishers, 1988.
   Children's Creative Response to Conflict, an organization with Quaker roots, developed this resource. It contains suggestions and activities for building community, learning to communicate and to cooperate, and for promoting self-awareness and empathy. Available from the publisher: P.O. Box 582, Santa Cruz, California 95061.

Lesson Resources

Lesson 1
Aliki. *Manners.* New York: Greenwillow, 1990.
   Amusing illustrations and a handwritten text combine for a delightful look at manners.

Berenstain, Stan and Jan. *The Berenstain Bears Forget Their Manners.* New York: Random, 1986.

Berry, Joy W. *What to Do When Your Mom or Dad Says … "What Should You Say Dear?"* Chicago: Childrens Press, no date.

Brown, Marc, and Stephen Krensky. *Perfect Pigs: An Introduction to Manners.* New York: Atlantic Monthly Press, 1983.

Dellinger, Annetta E. *Good Manners for God's Children.* St. Louis: Concordia, 1984.

Hoban, Russell. *Dinner at Alberta's.* New York: Harper, 1975.
   Because Arthur the crocodile eats like a beast, his family is trying to shape up his table manners for dinner at Alberta's.

Leaf, Munro. *Manners Can Be Fun.* 3rd ed. New York: Harper Junior Books, 1985.

Moncure, Jane. *Excuse Me.* Chicago: Childrens Press, 1989.

Odor, Ruth S. *A Child's Book of Manners.* Cincinnati, Ohio: Standard, 1990.

Simon, Norma. *What Do I Say?* Niles, Ill.: Whitman, 1983.

Lessons 2-3
Micallef, Mary. *Listening: The Basic Connection.* Carthage, Ill.: Good Apple, 1984.
   Contains reproducible activities that cover listening awareness, motivation, and related topics. Although the activities are intended for grades 3-8, teachers may find ideas to adopt.

Lesson 4
Hoban, Lillian. *Don't Eat Too Much Turkey!* New York: Macmillan, 1971.

Keats, Ezra. *Peter's Chair.* New York: Harper, 1967.

Lionni, Leo. *It's Mine.* New York: Knopf, 1986.

Udry, Janice. *What Mary Jo Shared.* Niles, Ill. Whitman, 1966.

Waber, Bernard. *Bernard.* Boston: Houghton, 1982.

Ziefert, Harriet. *Me, Too! Me, Too!* New York: Harper, 1988.

Lesson 5

Beim, Lorraine and Jerrold. *Two Is a Team*. New York: Harcourt, 1945.
    Although out of print, this classic may be available at libraries.

Cohen, Miriam. *Best Friends*. New York: Macmillan, 1971.
    When the light in the classroom incubator goes out, two friends work together to save a science experiment.

Goffstein, M.B. *Our Snowman*. New York: Harper, 1986.

Lionni, Leo. *Swimmy*. New York: Knopf, 1973, 1987.
    A small fish joins with other small fish to defeat a menacing shark.

LESSON 1: YES, THANK YOU

Preparation/Materials
- Chart paper
- Materials for bulletin board or beginning reader newspaper (see step 3)

Objectives
- Students will understand the purpose of good manners.
- Students will identify specific good manners.
- Students will practice using good manners.

Background
Good manners and courtesy express concern for others. If we love our neighbors, we will clean up our own mess, show appreciation for their help, and say we're sorry when we hurt their feelings or damage their belongings. It's important for students to understand this root of good manners. The stress in this lesson should be on loving others and not on learning a rigid set of rules. Still, every society has a set of rules that govern social situations. Knowing what is acceptable behavior and practicing social skills helps children feel at ease socially and gives them self-confidence.

● ●

Lesson

1. Make an experience chart of good manners. When do children usually say *please, thank you,* and *you're welcome* (you may want to add *excuse me* and *sorry*). Talk about the reason for saying these things.

2. Give children the opportunity to practice using good manners. Act out simple situations with class members (or invite older students to do the acting) that demonstrate the proper use of the "magic" words identified in step 1. Also practice greeting people politely. For example, pretend to be another school staff member and have students greet you correctly, using your name and proper title (Mr., Ms., or Mrs.). Practice situations until students feel comfortable using polite greetings.

3. As a way to reinforce the lesson, have students be "good manners detectives," reporting when they see or hear others using good manners. Find a creative way to record their reports. Make a beginning reader newspaper. Enter every report in a sentence. ("Chris thanked me for helping him.") Keep the newspaper at a center for students to read and enjoy. Or consider making a "please and thank you" tree on the bulletin board. Mount a large construction paper tree trunk on the bulletin board and for every please or thank reported, add a leaf to the tree. See how quickly the class can complete the tree.

4. **Closure.** Refer to the experience chart. Ask: "Why is saying thank you (excuse me, sorry) important?"

● ●

Related Activities

1. Read books about good manners:
   Manners by Aliki
   Excuse Me by Jane Moncure
   Perfect Pigs: An Introduction to Manners by
       Marc Brown and Stephen Krensky
   The Berenstain Bears Forget Their Manners by
       Stan and Jan Berenstain
   Good Manners for God's Children by Annetta
       E. Dellinger

   What Do I Say? by Norma Simon
   Manners Can Be Fun by Munro Leaf
   Dinner at Alberta's by Russell Hoban

2. Provide manipulatives at a center so that students can reenact social situations covered during the whole-class session.

LESSON 2: STOP, LOOK, AND LISTEN!

Preparation/Materials

- Make three signs: on one write *STOP* and draw a hand raised in the stop sign, on the second write *LOOK* and draw a pair of eyes, on the third write *LISTEN* and draw a large ear.

Objectives

- Students will recognize the importance of listening to others.
- Students will identify a good listening procedure.
- Students will practice the listening procedure.

Background

"Listening is a skill that can be learned and an art that can be mastered …. We owe it to ourselves to make it our best language art!" This quotation from a popular book on teaching listening to children turns the purpose of listening on its head. Listening is not something we owe to ourselves. Listening to others is one way of loving them. Active listening means that we are receptive to others, that we value them and their ideas. This lesson and the next try to make students aware of what's involved in listening and why it's important, helping them practice and improve their listening skills. But keep the emphasis of these lessons straight, for although learning listening skills can make us more conscious of what's going on in the communication process, skills are no substitute for sincere interest and concern.

These two lessons teach a three-step listening procedure. Students are taught to stop what they're doing and pay attention, to look at the speaker, and then to actively listen to what's being said. Consider using this STOP, LOOK, and LISTEN procedure at various times throughout the day (particularly during this unit) to encourage good listening habits.

Lesson

1. Ask each child to think of a favorite song or story or game. Then at your signal, have them all at the same time say what their favorite is.

2. Ask several students to identify the favorites of other class members. Since all have been talking and not listening, most likely they won't know. Lead students to understand that's why they can't identify others' favorites. Talk about why it's important to listen to others. Tell them that in this lesson they will practice being good listeners.

3. Hold up the STOP, LOOK, and LISTEN signs and teach the class the words. Explain that in order to be good listeners, we have to stop moving and talking, pay attention to the speaker, and listen to what he or she is saying.

4. Practice the stop, look, and listen procedure with the class. Ask students to pretend to be airplanes or boats and "travel" around the room. At intervals hold up the signs. Have them stop moving, look at your sign, and listen to your message ("Try flying on tiptoes" or "Let's dip our wings" or "Let's blow our ship's horn").

5. **Closure.** Briefly recap the lesson. Ask students how they can be good listeners and ask them what the signs mean.

● ●

Related Activities

* Sing an echo song in which the class listens to the teacher singing a line and then repeats what the teacher sings. "Are You Sleeping?" is an echo song most children know. Make up words to fit with the lesson's theme.

I'm a good listener. (children echo/repeat)
Yes, I am! (echo)
I stop, look, and listen. (echo)
Yes, I do! (echo)
Or try echo clapping. Clap a rhythm pattern and have the class repeat it.

LESSON 3: LISTENING TO LEARN ABOUT EACH OTHER

Preparation/Materials

- Stop, Look, and Listen signs from previous lesson
- Optional: chart paper

Objectives

- Students will practice listening to each other.
- Students will identify the characteristics of listening to others.

Lesson

1. Use the signs to review the listening procedure. Tell students that today they will practice listening to each other.

2. **Student activity.** Divide the class into pairs or small groups. Explain that the students will take turns talking and listening to each other. The listener should try to learn at least one new thing about the speaker.

   First, demonstrate the activity with the help of a student. Then have the class brainstorm a list of possible questions they could ask each other (Do you have any sisters or brothers? What is one of your favorite places to go? What do you like to do at recess? What is your favorite food?) Write these on a chart or chalkboard for the students to refer to during the activity. Encourage them to ask anything else they think of during the actual interview.

   Have students interview each other. After a short time hold up the signs as a signal for students to reverse roles.

3. **Circle talk.** Gather students into a circle and have them share new things they learned about class members by listening. Close the lesson by asking students to identify what they did when they listened.

Related Activities

- Have pairs of students do an activity in which one gives directions and the other follows them. For example, drawing and/or coloring designs (perhaps have them draw square and triangle shapes to build a listening tower). Both students make the drawing; the one following the directions should not be able to see the work of the one giving directions. Do the activity twice and have students switch roles.

73

LESSON 4: HEY, HEY, WHAT CAN WE SHARE?

Preparation/Materials
- Story about sharing to read to the class
- For the student activity:
  large piece of clay (about two pounds)
  plastic knife
  pair of child's scissors
  a 12" length of wire
  table with five chairs
- Optional: fruit and napkins for class snack

Objectives
- Students will become aware of the importance of sharing.
- Students will identify ways to share.

Background
Because egocentrism is a normal characteristic of early childhood, sharing is a very difficult concept for young children to grasp. Some think sharing means that others should give them what they want; some only see that they must give up something. Children begin to understand sharing by learning to take turns and by seeing how other children enjoy their turns. Gradually they come to understand the position and viewpoint of another person. Use this lesson to encourage them in the direction of sharing, of loving their neighbors.

• •

Lesson

1. Begin the lesson by sharing something with the class. For example, cut up some pieces of fruit and pass them around.

2. **Circle talk.** Have students identify what and how you shared. Talk about the reason we share and why it's hard to share. Teach or review the word *share.*

3. Read a story about sharing. Suggested titles:
   Don't Eat Too Much Turkey! by Lillian Hoban
   What Mary Jo Shared by Janice Udry
   Peter's Chair by Ezra Keats
   It's Mine by Leo Lionni
   Bernard by Bernard Waber
   Me, Too! Me, Too! by Harriet Ziefert

   Or tell an appropriate Bible story such as the story of Tabitha who made clothes for the needy (Acts 9:36-42) or of the widow of Zarephath who shared the little food she had with Elijah (1 Kings 17:7-16).

4. Make up a song about sharing. Have students suggest things to share and then make up the verses as you go along. The tune of "Skip to My Lou" works well.
   The teacher asks the question:

   Hey, hey, what can we share? (three times)
   What can we share with others?

And the students reply:

> We can share our games and toys. (three times)
> That's what we can share with others.

On each new verse, use students suggestions to change the reply.

You may also wish to sing or listen to Raffi's "The Sharing Song" (p. 76 in *Singable Songbook* or the record/audiocassette *Singable Songs for the Very Young*).

5. **Student activity.** Sharing in everyday activities requires problem-solving skills. This structured activity gives the class opportunity to cooperate in solving a problem about sharing a large lump of clay.

   Sit at a table with four students. Provide a plastic knife, a child's scissors, and a 12″ length of wire as tools for dividing the clay. The students must decide which tools to use and how to divide the clay fairly. Put the lump of clay in the center of the table, but "neutralize" it by keeping your hand on it.

   Explain the problem: there is one piece of clay and four children who want to use it. How can they all use it?

   Elicit ideas from the students, if necessary clarifying what they say for the rest of the class. Students should retain responsibility for solving the problem during the discussion. Encourage them to critique each other's ideas. When they do arrive at a solution, carry it out together. Praise students for their problem-solving skills and briefly summarize what took place (problem solving and solution).

   (This activity is adapted from the book *Teaching Young Children Using Themes* [Good Year, 1991].)

6. **Closure:** "Today we talked about ways we can share with others. Why is it hard to share? Why do you think we should share?"

● ●

Related Activities

1. Center idea: set up a sharing center with toys and games that two or more children can play with or, better yet, that *need* two or more to play.

2. Find a way for the class to share with others. This can be a one-time service activity such as making and serving popcorn to another class or it can be an ongoing project such as bringing grocery items to class to contribute to a local food bank.

LESSON 5: LEARNING TO COOPERATE

Preparation/Materials

- Obtain items for cooperative activity of your choice (see step 2)
- Student Activities 1 & 2
- Optional: art materials for illustrating class story

Objectives

- Students will understand the concept of co-operating.
- Students will practice cooperating.

• •

Lesson

1. Review the concept of cooperating. Teach the word *cooperate*. Explain that by working together people can do many things that they can't do alone. Name an activity and ask students to tell whether it takes one person or more than one (brushing teeth, riding a bicycle, seesawing, playing in a band, acting out a play, playing house, driving a car, carrying a large piece of classroom furniture).

2. Do one or more activities that require cooperation. Consider using one of the following suggestions:

   - Enlist the class's cooperation to take care of some classroom housekeeping tasks. Have them sort crayons or other materials and/or work in pairs or groups to clean their storage areas and tables. Assign each child a specific task such as getting water, wiping a table, or sorting certain objects. Compliment students on their work and note when the job is finished how much better things go when all cooperate.

   - Have a scavenger hunt. Divide the class into groups and give each group a picture list of items hidden around the room for them to find. (Hide the items before class.) Instead of making this a competitive game, give each group a different set of items. Each team should have a bag or box in which to place the items they find. During the search encourage team members to help each other so that each member gets a chance to find one item.

   - Make snacks. Have some students mix juice, some put a cheese spread or peanut butter on crackers, and others make fruit kabobs. Then sit down and enjoy the "fruits" of cooperation. If you have invited parents to help with this activity, point out how their cooperation helped make the snacks possible.

   - Discuss the pictures on the student activity pages and have students identify which kids are sharing and cooperating, which ones need help, which ones are using good manners and/or sharing. Have the students color the pictures.

3. To integrate with language arts and reinforce the idea of cooperating, write a class story about the just-completed activity. If time permits, have students draw or paint illustrations to go with the story.

4. **Closure:** "Today we had a good time cooperating. Why do you think we should cooperate with each other? What would happen if we didn't cooperate?

● ●
Related Activities

1. Read stories on the lesson topic: *Our Snowman* by M.B. Goffstein, *Two Is a Team* by Lorraine and Jerrold Beim, *Swimmy* by Leo Lionni, *Best Friends* by Miriam Cohen.

2. Integrate with social studies by studying how community members cooperate to provide services.

3. Have paper dolls or other manipulatives available at a center so students can act out ways people cooperate at school, at home, or in the community. They can also reenact how they cooperated to clean up the classroom, complete the scavenger hunt, or make the snacks.

4. Center idea: set up a Transportation Cooperation Station. Collect empty food cartons, styrofoam meat trays, paper tubes, egg cartons, and so on. Provide glue. A student coming to the center must work with at least one other person to create a form of transportation. It might be a boat, train, plane, car, bus, or spaceship. This will give class members additional practice in problem solving, sharing, and cooperating.

5. Tie in a physical activity at gym or on the playground. Provide a tire or inner tube. Assign teams to push or roll it toward a goal. The pair that cooperates will have the easiest time reaching the goal. Or, if the weather permits, form an outdoor bucket brigade relay. (You may want to send a note home warning parents the children will get wet with this one.)

Unit 4

My Amazing Body

Goals

- Students will develop body awareness.
- Students will become aware of how amazing the human body is.
- Students will acknowledge and praise God as their Creator.

Background

In *Beyond Doubt* (Christian Reformed Board of Publications, 1980) Cornelius Plantinga tells an anecdote about Whittaker Chambers, a dedicated atheist. One day when Chambers was watching his child as she sat in her high chair, "he found himself staring with fascination at his daughter's tiny, intricate ear. It seemed to him a marvel. Only a *planner* could have planned that ear." This experience "set Chambers on the road to belief."

The human body is truly amazing. And it's very smart. In fact, it's brilliant. It performs to a large extent "on its own." The heart beats, lungs breathe, stomach digests, kidneys purify—all without our even thinking about it. When we study the human body—its parts, processes, growth, and development—we cannot help but wonder at the complexity of its design. Our study should lead us to marvel not only at the body, but at the God who created it.

God has given us life, and that life is mysteriously and inextricably linked to a body so complex that we will never completely understand it. Our fitting response is awe and wonder and praise to God, the Creator. "I will praise you," said the Psalmist, "because I am fearfully and wonderfully made; your works are wonderful, I know that full well" (Psalm 139:14).

Vocabulary

Integrate the following suggested vocabulary:

freeze	hands	lungs	intestines	digest
senses	nose	stomach	blood	hinge
looks	toes	brain	world	window
smells	shoulders	heart	joint	buttocks
feels	clap	organ(s)	grow	machine
sounds	chest	body	back	tastes

Lesson Resources

Lesson 1

Charters, Jill, and Ann Gately. *Drama Anytime.* Rozelle, Australia: Primary English Teaching Association, 1986.

> This resource contains a number of cooperative exercises and movement suggestions. The book is distributed by Heinemann, 70 Court St., Portsmouth, New Hampshire 03801.

Nilsson, Lennart. *A Child Is Born: The Completely New Edition.* New York: Delacorte, 1990.

Lesson 2

Aliki. *My Five Senses*. New York: Crowell, 1962.

Henry, Lucia Kemp. *Science and Ourselves: Worksheets and Activities to Explore the Human Body*. New York: Fearon Teacher Aids/Simon and Schuster Group, 1989.
    Intended for grades 1-3, this teacher resource contains 18 pages of reproducible materials on the senses.

Lungs Are for Life—1. Kit. American Lung Association, 1983.
    Although the focus of the kit is lung health, Unit 3 has material on the five senses. The kit contains a teacher guide, reproducible activity sheets, read-along booklet, and audiocassette. Contact a local American Lung Association chapter in the U.S. to obtain the kit.

Moncure, Jane. *What Your Nose Knows!* Chicago: Childrens Press, 1982.

Our Senses Work Together. Filmstrip. Bambi Discovers the Five Senses Set. Disney Educational Products.
    This ten-minute filmstrip shows Bambi finding out about his senses.

Rius, Maria, J.J. Puig, and J.M. Parramón. Series on the Five Senses. Toronto/New York: Barron's, 1985.

Thigpen, Thomas. *Colors of Creation*. Weston, Ont./Elgin, Ill.: Cook, 1990.

Your Tongue Is for Tasting. Filmstrip/audiocassette. Random House.
    A nine-minute film helping students recognize four kinds of taste and appreciate the role of taste in daily living.

Lessons 3-5

Bruun, Ruth D. and Bertel. *The Human Body*. Random House Library of Knowledge. New York: Random, 1982.
    This book, intended for grades 5 and up, is a helpful teacher resource.

Freeberg, Lois. *Learning About Your Body: Grades 1-2*. Palos Verdes Estates, California: Frank Schaffer Publications, 1988.
    Contains reproducible worksheets on basic anatomy.

My Wonderful Body Machine. Filmstrip/audiocassette. New York: American Cancer Society, 1977.
    The American Cancer Society makes available free of charge a multimedia kit (filmstrip, cassette, poster, reproducible activity sheets) consisting of four teaching units. The unit My Body, intended for kindergarten, fits well with these unit lessons. The unit includes the sound filmstrip *My Wonderful Body Machine*. Contact a local chapter of the Cancer Society in the U.S. to obtain the kit.

Putting It All Together. Filmstrip/audiocassette. Bowmar-Noble.
    Shows how the parts of the body work together.

Showers, Paul. *A Drop of Blood*. New York: Harper, 1989.

_____. *Hear Your Heart*. New York: Harper, 1968.

_____. *What Happens to a Hamburger*. New York: Harper, 1968.

Lesson 6

Raffi. *Raffi Singable Songbook*. New York: Crown, 1988.

The song "I Wonder If I'm Growing" ties in with the lesson theme. The song is also available on audiocassette.

LESSON 1: FEARFULLY AND WONDERFULLY MADE

Preparation/Materials

- Optional: Music to accompany creative movement activity

Objectives

- Students will develop a sense of wonder at the way God created them.
- Students will praise and give thanks to God for the gift of life.

Lesson

1. Introduce the unit with a few body awareness activities. Students should sit on the floor and try to move one isolated part of the body at a time. Have them begin by moving only their toes (without shoes is best); then have them gradually work up the body (ankles, knees, hips, back, shoulder, arms, and head). Tell the class that you will say the word *freeze* when you want them to stop moving. Freeze between moving each body part. Encourage the children to move each part in as many ways as they can.

   Then ask class members to pretend that they have a fly on the end of their nose. They must try to make the fly fly away by moving that body part (no using hands). But then the fly moves to another body part (shoulder ear, elbow, knee, etc.), and they have to wiggle that part. If you wish, sing "Shoo Fly Don't Bother Me" during this activity.

   (These two body awareness activities are adapted from *Drama Anytime* by Jill Charters and Anne Gately.)

2. Next have the class move to music. Together sing and do the accompanying actions to "Here We Go Looby Lou" or "The Hokey Pokey."

3. Say this rhyme by Marian Grayson and have students mime the actions:

   Hands on Shoulders
   Hands on shoulders; hands on knees,
   Hands behind you, if you please;
   Touch your shoulders, now your nose,
   Now your hair and now your toes;
   Hands up high in the air,
   Down at your sides and touch your hair;
   Hands up high as before,
   Now clap your hands, one, two, three, four.

5. **Circle talk.** This is a good time to talk about how amazing our bodies are, how wonderfully God has made us. Paraphrase Psalm 139:13-14. Tell students about the amazing way they developed even before they were born. When they were still tiny, smaller than your little finger, they already had arms and hands, a brain, and a beating heart.

Note that God has made us in such a way that our bodies grow. We need new clothes every year, but we don't need new skin every year because our skin (and other parts of the body) keep growing. (If possible, illustrate this discussion with Lennart Nilsson's marvelous photographs in the book *A Child Is Born*.)

6. Conclude by thanking God for creating us and caring for us. Teach students the song "I Can." Sing the song frequently during the unit.

I Can

LESSON 2: WINDOWS ON GOD'S WORLD

Preparation/Materials

- Object to describe (preferably something edible), one object per student
- Make a chart of the five senses:

A Marshmallow ...	
looks	_____
smells	_____
feels	_____
sounds	_____
tastes	_____

- For Our Senses mural:

  paper cut in shape of talking balloon, one balloon per student

  strips of mural paper, enough to outline each student (about 4-5 students to a strip to keep length manageable)

Objectives

- Students will review the five senses.
- Students will identify how their senses keep them safe.

Background

This lesson is based on the American Lung Association's kit, *Lungs Are For Life-1*, Unit 3.

Lesson

1. Fill in the chart with the class. Begin by displaying the chart and asking students to identify each sense organ and what it does. Next, give each student an object to describe, preferably something edible. Have students place the object in front of them and carefully look at it. Ask the class members to describe the object. Brainstorm words as a class. Refer to the chart and take one sense at a time. How does their prune or piece of apple look, smell, feel, sound, and taste? Write the words on the chart. Encourage creativity. If the object is edible, let students eat it before describing "taste."

   Note that God not only made us in a wonderful way, but God also made the world. And it's through the five senses that we find out about God's world. Describe why our senses can be called our "windows" on God's world.

2. **Student activity.** Make a class mural entitled Our Senses. Trace the outlines of class members on lengths of mural paper. To keep strips of manageable length draw about five or six student shapes on each piece. Leave enough room on the strip between body outlines for students to attach a talking balloon. Students can personalize the outlines, coloring in facial features, hair, and clothing.

   Have each student write on a talking balloon a statement telling something he or she likes to see, hear, smell, taste, or feel, and then attach the balloon on the mural paper (see illustration).

Display the mural strips. Discuss the completed display with the class and ask students to read and explain their statement about one of their senses.

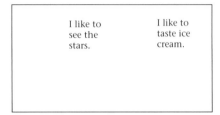

I like to see the stars.

I like to taste ice cream.

3. **Closure**. Summarize and evaluate with the following questions:
   - "How many senses do we have?"
   - "What are they?"
   - "How are our senses our 'windows' on God's world?"

• •

Related Activities

1. Enjoy books on the five senses with the class. A series of five books on the senses by Rius, Puig, and Parramón is available. Other titles:
   What Your Nose Knows! by Jane Moncure
   Is It Rough? Is It Smooth? Is It Shiny? by Tana Hoban
   Colors of Creation by Thomas Thigpen
   My Five Senses by Aliki

2. Take the class for "sense" walks inside the school building or around the neighborhood. You may wish to choose one sense for them to focus on for each walk. After returning to the classroom, give students opportunity to talk and write about what they saw, smelled, touched, or heard.

3. Use the words on the senses chart for language arts activities. Write a class poem about the object students described. Or use the words for a sentence-building activity.

4. Make booklets on the five senses. Divide the class into groups and have each group put together a shape booklet on one of the senses. For example, the booklet about the sense of smell could be in a nose shape, and each child in the group could contribute a picture of something that smells good.

5. Show a filmstrip about the senses. One suggestion is *Our Senses Work Together* from the series Bambi Discovers the Five Senses.

LESSON 3: HINGES AND JOINTS

Preparation/Materials
- Student Activities 1 & 2
- Hole punch
- Paper fasteners, ten per student
- Hinge or object using a hinge (for example, a small box with hinged cover)

Objective
- Students will identify some important body joints.

• •

Lesson

1. **Student Activity.** Direct students to cut out the puppets on the Student Activity sheets and to put them together with fasteners. Keep the puppets handy to use during the lesson.

2. Show students the hinge and how it operates. Explain how the hinge works.

   Ask students if they have hinges in their body. Ask them to take out the puppets they made and see if they can find any hinges. Have them move the parts up and down.

3. Demonstrate the importance of joints, of being able to bend. Have the children stand and pretend to step over an imaginary object in front of them. Dramatize the situation; describe the object in some detail (prickly porcupine or sleeping skunk). Stop the children halfway into the step so that they can see the bending movement at the knee. Next, tell them to try to step over the object straightlegged, without bending at the knee. Also point out or demonstrate the bending action necessary for sitting or for bringing food to the mouth.

4. Ask the class to bend whatever part of the body they can. Identify the joint in elbows, knees, and jaws as hinge joints. Note that they have more joints than the puppets. See if they can find other locations of joints—in fingers, toes, or wrist. Explain that hinge joints are only one kind of joint found in the body. (Other types are ball and socket joints, gliding joints, and pivoting joints.)

5. Sing an action song about bending. Make up a simple verse or sing the following to the tune of "Did You Ever See a Lassie?"
   > Can you bend your finger, your finger, your finger?
   > Can you bend your finger?
   > Now you show me how!

   Substitute different bendable body parts in subsequent verses. Have students respond with an appropriate action.

6. Then have a good time singing the song "Hinges."

7. **Closure:** "We learned about our hinges, our joints, today. We found out that we need our joints to be able to do all kinds of things. (Elicit examples from students.) Our bodies are really amazing!"

Build reading or spelling vocabulary with a labeling activity. Make an enlarged tagboard version of the student puppet and name cards for body parts (include neck, shoulder, elbow, wrist, buttocks, ankle, thigh). Ask volunteers to come up one at a time, pick a name card and fasten it to the correct body part with a paper clip. If you wish, you can remove the cards and have another group of volunteers repeat the activity.

Hinges

LESSON 4: LOOKING INSIDE

Preparation/Materials

- Student Activities 1a–1d
- Paper for making body tracings of class members. (If you prefer, provide a "generic" body outline for each child.)
- Student Activities 2a & 2b. Consider using a different color of construction paper for each body section.
- Student Activity 3
- Optional, but recommended: obtain an animal heart (chicken, cow, or sheep) from the butcher.

Objective

- Students will identify the location and basic function of the brain, heart, lungs, and stomach and intestines.

Background

In this lesson students are introduced to basic body organs. They learn the location of each in the body and the simple function of each. (Note: lungs are studied in more detail in Unit 7, Lesson 6.)

Student Activity 1a—Heart. The heart is the pump that moves blood through the body. The beating of the heart is the sound of the heart working, pumping the blood in and out. The blood the heart pumps out (through arteries) is full of oxygen. The blood carries the oxygen through miles of tubes to every part of the body—to the head, to the ends of the fingers, and down to the toes. Then the blood, now oxygen poor, travels back through veins to be re-loaded with oxygen.

Student Activity 1b—Lungs. The body gets the oxygen it needs from the air. When we breathe in, the air moves in through our nose or mouth and goes down the windpipe into our lungs. (The little hairs in our nose clean the air and the wetness in our mouth and throat also traps germs.) The lungs work like balloons; they get bigger when we breathe in and smaller when we breathe out. The lungs have tiny sacs in them. The oxygen goes from the sacs into the blood.

Student Activity 1c—Stomach and intestines. How does our body use the food we eat to give us energy and help us grow? First we chew the food into bits—until it's small enough to swallow. Then the muscles in the throat move the food down a tube into the stomach. The stomach, which is made of muscle, mixes up the food until it becomes mushy. The mushy food moves on into the intestines. In the intestines the food moves into the blood. (You may wish to explain that the body gets rid of the food parts it can't use when we go to the bathroom.)

Student Activity 1d—Brain. The brain is the control center of the body. It helps us respond to the world around us. It helps us move, touch, smell, speak, hear, taste, and see. We think and read and solve problems with our brain. And we remember things and invent new ideas with it, too. The brain is soft, and it is protected by bone (the skull). Brain cells that have been destroyed by injury, disease, or birth defects cannot grow back.

Lesson (2-3 sessions)

1. Tell students that in this lesson they're going to learn something about the inside of their bodies. Trace body outlines of the class members (or give each child a basic body shape). Explain that after you discuss each body part and find out what it does, the students will put the body part where it belongs on the shape. Consider having the students cut out all the body organs (Student Activities 2a and 2b) at this time, too.

2. Discuss each body organ. Have the students turn to their visuals and use the background information to explain how each organ functions. After completing each section, have students tape or glue the organ(s) into place on their body shapes.

Heart. Begin by asking students what the heart is and what it does. Compare the heart to a pump and note that the heart is always working. It works harder when we're active and it can "rest" when we do. Have students try to feel their heartbeat and describe the heart's rhythm. Also have them find the veins in their wrists and identify these as part of the "tube" system that carries the blood in the body.

Students are fascinated by the opportunity to see an actual heart. If you have obtained an animal heart, spend time discussing and, if possible, dissecting it. You may wish to consider asking a science teacher to do this activity with the class.

Lungs. Ask students to take some deep breaths. Ask: "What happens when we breathe?" Explain that air is going in and then out of our lungs. Show the visual and have students identify where the air comes in and trace its path down the windpipe and to the lungs. Note from the first visual how the lungs and heart are closely connected.

Stomach and intestines. Ask: "Where does our food go after we eat it?" Use the visual to trace the path the food follows. In explaining the digestive process, consider noting that newborns only drink milk at first because they don't have teeth to chew the food and their digestive organs can't handle solid food.

Brain. Ask: "What does the brain do?" Identify the brain on the visual. Explains its function. Note that we take in information through our senses, and then our brain uses this information and tells us what to do. Consider brainstorming a list of things the brain can do.

3. **Student Activity 3.** Have students complete the crossword puzzle. Go over the completed worksheet and review the function of the organs.

4. **Closure:** "In this lesson we learned more about the amazing bodies God has given us. We took a peek inside and we learned the names of some important parts of the body and what these parts do." (Elicit names of organs and the basic function of each.)

• •

Related Activities

1. Center idea: obtain one or more stethoscopes and have students use them to listen to their heartbeat. Students can also learn to feel their pulse (older students could help with this activity).

2. Read one or more of Paul Showers' books about the body: *Drop of Blood, Hear Your Heart,* or *What Happens to a Hamburger.*

3. Use a blender to demonstrate how the stomach works. Blend some vegetables or fruits with a small amount of water. Explain that juices in the stomach together with movement of the stomach muscles help to make the food a mushy consistency.

4. Make a large puzzle of a body shape with organs placed correctly and put it at the center for students to assemble.

LESSON 5: THE BODY MACHINE

Preparation/Materials
- A simple machine: can opener, grinder, or pencil sharpener
- Art materials and paper for making class booklet

Objective
- Students will recognize that the various parts of the body work together.

• •

Lesson

1. Show students a simple machine such as a can opener, small grinder or chopper, or pencil sharpener. Demonstrate how it works: open a can or sharpen a pencil. Point out how the different parts work together to get the job done.

2. Make a comparison to the body: the body is like a wonderful machine with many parts that work together. Have students name some of the body parts they have studied in this unit. Ask: "How do the parts work together?" Give examples (the eye sees food; the hand reaches for it and puts it in the mouth; the mouth chews). Illustrate the example by drawing stick figures on the board. Point out that our body parts work together in such a wonderful way that we're hardly aware of what is going on. We even sleep while our heart keeps pumping blood and lungs keep breathing.

   Then ask: "How are we *more* than a machine (refer to the pencil sharpener or can opener used for demonstration)?" (We are created in God's image. We can talk and we can love others—and God.)

3. Improvise a song about how the parts of the body work together. Use the folksong "What Shall We Do When We All Go Out?" found at the end of the lesson. Adapt the tune slightly to make the words fit.

4. **Student activity.** Write lists of things we can do with the bodies God gave us. On the board write the following sentence starter:

   With my body, I can ....

   Ask students to think of as many things they can do as possible (ride, pull, climb, slide, jump, dig, look for something, watch something, lie down, sit, swim, talk, sing).

   Then use the list to make a class booklet with each child illustrating a different body action. Encourage them to write captions using the "action" word on the list.

   Or if the class enjoyed the piggyback song in step 3, sing the folksong's original words and ask students to use the verbs on the list to make up subsequent verses.

5. **Closure.** Summarize and evaluate with these questions:
   - "What is this called?" (Show machine from step 1.)
   - "How is your body like a machine?"
   - "How is it different from a machine?"

• •

Related Activities

- A number of films are available on how the body works. Show the class a film such as *Putting It All Together* or *My Wonderful Body Machine*.

I See the Food

Moderately Fast

North Carolina

Health version:

1. I see the fo-o-d with my eyes, with my eyes,
    with my eyes,
    I see the fo-o-d with my eyes, and I can
    smell it, too.
2. I pick up the fo-o-d with my hand, with my
    hand, with my hand,
    I pick up the fo-o-d with my hand, and pop
    it in my mouth.
3. With my teeth I chew-chew-chew, chew-
    chew-chew, chew-chew-chew,
    With my teeth I chew-chew-chew. Mmmm-
    mmmmmmm, it's good.
4. I take a swallow and down food goes, down
    it goes, down it goes,
    I take a swallow and down food goes, right
    into my stomach.
5. Stomach gets to work and digests the food,
    works and works, digests the food,
    Stomach gets to work and digests the food.
    I've got energy.
6. Oh, what a wonderful body machine, body
    machine, body machine,
    Oh, what a wonderful body machine. Now
    let's shout "Hooray!"

    (All give a shout and clap.)

Other suggested verses:

1. My lungs keep breathing all the time, etc.,
    Air goes in and out.
2. My brain tells my body what to do, etc.,
    And it's right up in my head.
3. My heart is a pump, and it pumps my
    blood, etc.,
    I can feel it go thump, thump.
4. Shall I tell you one more thing, etc.,
    I have joints that help me bend.

Folksong words:

What shall we do when we all go out,
All go out, all go out,
What shall we do when we all go out,
When we all go out to play?

Verse using "action" word:

We will ride on the merry-go-round,
Merry-go-round, merry-go-round,
We will ride on the merry-go-round
When we all go out to play.

LESSON 6: WE ARE GROWING

Preparation/Materials
- Health puppets
- Student Activity 1 (Unit 2) showing living and nonliving things.
- For weighing activity:
  scales and a measuring stick
  Student Activity
  optional: older students, parents, or school staff to help weigh and measure
- Optional: object weighing one pound or one kilogram
- Optional: seeds or seedlings, soil, and containers for a classroom plant project

Objectives
- Students will recall the difference between living and nonliving things.
- Students will recognize that living things grow.
- Students will become aware of varying growth and development patterns.
- Students will predict their own growth pattern.

Background
First graders have some awareness of the growing process, but most of them have not thought about the process in any detail. Being aware of how their bodies grow will help them understand the importance of the health habits introduced in the next unit.

Lesson

1. Use Terry and Sam to spark a discussion of growing.

   Script suggestion:
   Terry: Do you think I'm getting taller, Sam?
   Sam: Taller? No-o-o, not really. Terry, you can't get taller.
   Terry: Why not? Look at the girls and boys right in front of us. They're taller now then the first time we saw them, aren't they?
   Sam: W-e-l-l, yes. I guess they are. (Consider making comments about specific children and how they've grown.)

   Have the puppets ask the class to explain why children grow and puppets don't. (Only living things grow.) Use questions such as the following to continue the discussion:
   - "Have you always been the size you are now?"
   - "How big do you think you'll be when you're grown up?"
   - "What makes you think you'll be that big?"
   - "Are people the only things in the world that change and grow after they're born?" (No, other living things—plants and animals—grow, too.)

2. Review the concept of living and nonliving things with the visual. Review the concept that living things grow. Predict how much the living things in the visual will grow.

3. Ask students if they are growing and will continue to grow. Ask how they know that they are growing. (They outgrow clothes; they can reach shelves that they couldn't reach when they were younger; they can actually see some parts of their body grow such as new teeth; they have to trim their hair and nails.) Explain that some parts of the body that they can't see are also alive and growing—for example, their bones, heart, lungs, stomach.

4. **Student activity.** Tell students that they are going to predict how much they will grow during the school year. Refer to the Student Activity sheet in the Student Workbook. Then weigh and measure the children and have them write the information and the date on the record sheet.

   Recall the concept of uniqueness of each person. Make the point that size and build are part of what makes each unique. First graders are different heights and weights now, and when they are fully grown, they will still be different sizes.

   Help the children make their growth predictions. Draw on the board the unit of measure—inch or centimeter. Engage students in a discussion of how many inches or centimeters a child their age might grow by the end of the school year. (A child may grow anywhere from 2 to about 6 inches.) Next, have students predict weight gains also. Lifting a one-pound or one-kilogram object may help them with this step. (A first grader will probably gain from 3 1/2 to 8 pounds). Students should write their predictions on the activity page in the space provided.

   Keep the record sheets, and at the end of the year weigh and measure again and check the predictions. Since for some children height and weight are a sensitive topic, avoid posting a chart with the facts and figures or making comparisons between students.

5. Point out how the class's plants have grown. If you did not have a plant-growing project for Unit 2 or if the plants are no longer in the classroom, consider beginning a "growing" project. As children observe the growth process, they become aware of what living plants need to grow: food, water, air, and rest (dormant period for plants). A plant project also makes a good companion to the next unit's lessons on the health needs of humans.

6. Close the lesson by singing "I Can" and/or Raffi's "I Wonder If I'm Growing."

7. Review unit concepts on growth and development.

Unit 5

Making Healthy Choices

Goals

- Students will identify and learn the importance of basic daily health choices.
- Students will begin to take responsibility for making good health choices.

Background

This unit deals with basic personal health care issues—fitness, nutrition, good grooming, and dental care. The stress is on helping students become aware of the health choices they make each day, so that from a young age they begin to assume responsibility for taking care of their bodies and form healthy patterns of living. But beyond developing basic living skills and healthy habits, students need to understand why taking care of bodies is important.

North American society sends confusing signals to children about the value of a person's body. On the one hand, there is the body cult, which makes an idol of the body. Shaping, strengthening, clothing, decorating, or gratifying the body is the central focus of some people's lives. This is a form of self-glorification and self-idolatry. On the other hand, our society has large numbers of persons who treat their bodies carelessly, ignoring basic nutrition and physical exercise or living at a too-strenuous pace. Carried to an extreme, this view leads to self-destruction. These contrasting views, however, share an underlying attitude that says: "This is my body. And what I do with my body is my business."

Christians believe that because "we are not our own," how we treat our body is not an individual matter. The kingly rule of Christ extends over the body, too. The body must not become an idol, but it should be treated with respect. After all, God created the human body and breathed life into it. In fact, God charged humans to be caretakers of that creation (Genesis 1:28). As God's people we are called to care for the body and use it in the service of God and others.

Vocabulary

Integrate the following suggested vocabulary:

choice	food	loose	brushing	delicious
fit	hand	tooth/teeth	nutrition	relax
exercise	heat	wish	dental floss	snack
big	fuel	dentist	sleep	cavity
small	energy	toothbrush	group	rest
great	engine	plaque		

Unit Resources

Color Me Red! Reston, Va.: American Alliance for Health Physical Education, Recreation & Dance. An activity book (K-3) about heart health. Order from AAHPERD, 1900 Association Drive, Reston, Virginia 22091; phone 800-321-0789.

Concepts for Feeling Good. Reston, Va.: AAHPERD. A handbook for adults providing background information on 12 important areas of wellness.

Cooper, Kenneth H. *Kid Fitness: A Complete Shape-Up Program from Birth Through High School.* New York: Bantam, 1991.

Cooper, concerned for this "generation of unfit children," has produced a total program of diet and exercise designed "to dramatically increase overall physical fitness and self-esteem and foster healthy eating habits." A checklist of tests is included to gauge the child's level of physical health.

Fitness Discovery Activities. Reston, Va.: AAHPERD.

"A series of 55 illustrated discovery activities help both adults and children learn about fitness, nutrition, stress, body composition, smoking, and other topics."

Palmer, Hap. *Learning Basic Skills, Vol. 3.* Audiocassette. Educational Activities.

Songs in volume 3 of this popular series include "Take a Bath," "Brush Away," and "Alice's Restaurant."

Lesson Resources

Lessons 2-3

Exercise and Rest. Film. Barr Films, 1983.

K-3 Games. Basic Skills Series. Gloucester, Ont.: Canadian Association for Health, Physical Education and Recreation (CAHPER).

This 100-page resource contains activities sequenced from simple to complex. Order from CAHPER, 1600 James Naismith Drive, Gloucester, Ontario K1B 5N4; phone 613-748-5622.

Palmer, Hap. *Learning Basic Skills Through Music, Vol. 3.* Educational Activities.

"Posture Exercises" and "Exercise Every Day" are two songs relating to the lesson.

Walk Like the Animals Record or audiocassette. KIMBO Educational.

Zuidema, Marvin, and others. *Physical Education K-2.* Grand Rapids: Christian Schools International, 1982.

Lesson 4

Brown, Margaret W. *Goodnight, Moon.* New York: Harper, 1934.

Hoban, Russell. *Bedtime for Frances.* New York: Harper, 1960.

Hopkins, Lee Bennett. *Still as a Star: A Book of Nighttime Poems.* Boston: Little, Brown, 1989.

Schotter, Roni. *Bunny's Night Out.* Boston: Joy Street Books, 1989.

After a series of adventures in the dark night, Bunny discovers the delight of a warm, cozy bed.

Waber, Bernard. *Ira Sleeps Over.* Boston: Houghton, 1972.

Lessons 5-7

Barrett, Judi. *Cloudy With a Chance of Meatballs.* New York: Macmillan, 1978.

A tale of a town where it rained food.

Berenstain, Stan and Jan. *The Bears' Picnic.* New York: Random House, 1966.

Eat Well, Grow Well. Coronet Films.

Food ... Your Choice, Grade 1. Kit. Rosemont, Ill.: National Dairy Council, 1987.

This kit contains a 40-page teacher guide, 24 food picture cards, a 2-part poster about where food comes from, and a story book. To order contact National Dairy Council, Nutrition Education Division, 6300 North River Road, Rosemont, Illinois 60019-9922.

Hines, Anna. *Daddy Makes the Best Spaghetti.* Boston: Houghton, 1986.

Hoban, Russell. *Bread and Jam for Frances.* New York: Harper, 1964.

Moncure, Jane. *What Was It Before It Was Bread?* Cincinnati: Child's World, 1985.

Rey, Margaret. *Curious George and the Pizza.* Boston: Houghton, 1985.

Sendak, Maurice. *Chicken Soup and Rice.* New York: Harper, 1962.

Watch What You Eat. Filmstrip/cassette. Topeka, Kansas
> A seven-minute film explaining the importance of knowing "which foods to eat and things that may be bad for you like certain poisons."

Lesson 8

Cleanliness. Film. Barr Films, 1985.

Cobb, Vicki. *Keeping Clean.* New York: Harper, 1989.

Munsch, Robert. *Mud Puddle.* Toronto: Annick Press, 1982.

Rub-a-Dub-Dub. Filmstrip/audiocassette. Disney Educational Products.
> A nine-minute film about the importance of cleanliness.

Zion, Gene. *Harry the Dirty Dog.* New York: Harper Trophy, 1976.

Lessons 9-10

Bate, Lucy. *Little Rabbit's Loose Tooth.* New York: Crown, 1975.

Berenstain, Stan and Jan. *The Berenstain Bears Visit the Dentist.* New York: Random, 1983.

Brown, Marc. *Arthur's Tooth.* Boston: Little, Brown 1980.

Cole, Joanna. *The Missing Tooth.* New York: Random, 1988.

Cooney, Nancy. *The Wobbly Tooth.* New York: Putnam, 1978.

Elementary School Dental Poster Set. Chicago: American Dental Association.
> Colorful posters available separately or in sets.

First Teeth. Ottawa: Canadian Dental Association.
> Kits for children that promote good dental health. Contact the Canadian Dental Association for the kits and a catalog of available materials: 1815 Alta Vista Dr., Ottawa, Ontario K1G 3Y6.

Learning About Your Oral Health: A Prevention-Oriented School Program, Level 1. Chicago: American Dental Association, 1980.
> Provides teaching units for grades K-3, including activities and several transparencies.

Linn, Margot. *A Trip to the Dentist.* New York: Harper, 1988.

McCloskey, Robert. *One Morning in Maine.* New York: Viking, 1952.

Meet Your Teeth. Filmstrip/audiocassette. Disney Educational Products.
> This filmstrip (seven-minute running time) explains what different types of teeth children will develop.

Mouth Models. Chicago: American Dental Association.
> Oversized models to demonstrate brushing techniques.

Rey, Margaret. *Curious George Goes to the Dentist.* Boston: Houghton Mifflin, 1989.

Rockwell, Harlow. *My Dentist.* New York: Greenwillow, 1975.

Ross, Pat. *Molly and the Slow Teeth.* New York: Lothrop, 1980.

Showers, Paul. *How Many Teeth?* Let's Read and Find Out Books. New York: Crowell, 1962.

Toothbrushing with Charlie Brown. Videocassette. Chicago: American Dental Association.
> This five-minute video is one of several videos on tooth care available from the Dental Association.

Why Visit the Dentist. Filmstrip/audiocassette. Disney Educational Products.
> This seven-minute filmstrip stresses the importance of seeing the dentist regularly.

LESSON 1: CHOICES, CHOICES, CHOICES

Preparation/Materials

- For shape booklet covers:
  construction paper or tagboard (skin color or color of choice). Cut covers in a circular shape to match shape of booklet/ student activity pages (see Lesson 3 student activity for pattern).
  art materials for decorating covers
- Make a sample front cover of smiling face. (Optional: decorate it to look like yourself.)
- Optional: health puppets

Objectives

- Students will become aware of their responsibility for their own health.
- Students will identify a variety of health choices they make each day.

Background

The unit project is a six-page beginning reader booklet about healthy choices. In this lesson students make the covers; in Lessons 3, 4, 5, 7, 8, and 10, they complete the booklet pages. Students assemble the booklet in Lesson 10 and use it for reviewing in Lesson 11.

We are suggesting a shape booklet with a happy face cover. Use one of the Student Activity pages as a pattern, or make the cover slightly larger than the booklet pages. Make the cover design a simple happy face, or if you prefer, have students put in their facial features and decorate the front cover to look like themselves. Join the completed booklet at the top with fasteners or staples. You may also wish to consider precutting the booklet pages for the class or having the class cut out all the pages at once.

• •

Lesson

1. Recall that in the last unit the class studied the body and the wonderful way God made us. Then tell students that God gives us responsibility for taking care of our bodies. We can make choices that help keep our bodies healthy.

2. Make students aware of some of their daily health choices. Act out or use one of the health puppets to act out a few situations that present health choices. Act puzzled (or have the puppet puzzle) over what choice to make and then ask class members for their opinion. Be dramatic and choose fairly obvious situations:
   - washing hands before eating a hot dog or eating with muddy hands
   - playing outside in cold or rainy weather with/without adequate clothing or footgear
   - leaving for school with/without washed face or brushed teeth
   - coughing or sneezing with mouth covered/uncovered
   - playing a video game or riding a bike

   After giving the class a few examples, invite volunteers to offer their own suggestions of healthy choices.

3. **Student activity.** Introduce the beginning reader booklet I Can. Write the words I Can on the board and explain they will be making a booklet about healthy choices they can make. Show students the sample cover.

Distribute the precut construction paper or tagboard covers and have students draw in a simple happy face or decorate the covers to look like themselves. (Keep in mind that the booklet will be joined at the top with fasteners or staples.)

4. **Closure:** "Today we talked about taking care of the bodies God gave us. Each day we can make choices that help keep our bodies healthy. In the next lessons we'll be talking about exercising, eating good food, and taking care of our teeth."

LESSON 2: STAYING FIT

Preparation/Materials
- For student activity:
  paper for painting or drawing, one sheet per
      student
  drawing or painting materials of choice
- Optional: music to accompany body movement activity
- Optional: music to accompany body movement activity

Objectives
- Students will identify ways to stay physically
  fit.
- Students will realize whole body movement.

Background
The American Alliance for Health, Physical
Education, Recreation and Dance (AAHPERD) has
a series called Basic Stuff that includes information about fitness and health for young children.

AAHPERD also has a program (1990) called Physical Best. This program includes lesson plans, an
awards program, and a computerized records program. These are excellent resources for teaching
fitness. The Physical Best awards program provides motivation for all children to work toward
greater fitness. There are, for example, awards for
exercising a certain amount every week and for
making a significant amount of improvement
during a period of time. All who work to improve
their fitness can receive awards.

Undoubtedly, children enjoy activity when
they are given the opportunity. However, too
often, children from an early age are funneled
into a youth sports program that caters to the
naturally athletic. To a large extent, the idea of
"free play" has been replaced with the idea that
exercise and play are organized activities. Instead,
creativity and fun in play should be encouraged.
This approach gives students a better understanding of and appreciation for their bodies.

Lesson
1. Have a "freedom of movement" session. Preferably use a large open space such as the
   school gymnasium or an outdoor play area. Tell the students to experiment with various body movements (sliding, walking on tiptoe, etc.). To avoid collisions, have children each establish a space of their own. Ask them to pretend they are in a space
   balloon or space bubble. As they move, they should avoid bumping into others' balloons or bubbles.

2. **Circle talk.** Give students time to talk about the session. What did they like about it?
   What kind of movements do they like? Note that different movements are fun for different people. Discuss fitness with the class. Teach the meaning of the word *fit* and explain that God has given us bodies that work best when they are fit. If our bodies are
   fit, we are able to enjoy activities, play, and work for a longer period of time. And if
   we're fit, we're less apt to get sick. To stay fit we have to move our bodies. When we
   move around, our heart goes faster and our muscles get stronger.

3. Brainstorm ways to keep fit. Make a list on the board. Include names of games, exercises students are familiar with, and common chores (walking to the store, dusting fur-

niture, picking up toys). If possible, have class members demonstrate the movement involved.

4. If time permits, have students draw or paint pictures of the movements they liked the best or of their feelings during the movement activity. Give opportunity for explaining the pictures to the rest of the class.

5. **Closure:** "We talked about being fit today. Why is it important to be fit? Are there some ways we can keep ourselves fit?"

● ●

Related Activities

- Send home an activity page for the students to complete. Students should do and record 15 minutes of exercise or movement a day for one month. Include a note to parents encouraging the whole family to participate.

LESSON 3: WORKING OUT

Preparation/Materials
- Student Activity page
- Choose which lesson exercises to use. Make arrangements to use the gym or gym equipment.

Objectives
- Students will recognize that humans are alike/different in motor skills.
- Students will develop motivation for exercising.

Background
The stress in this lesson is on helping students develop self-respect and on motivating them to use some of the lesson activities during playtime. Some of the suggested activities call for gym equipment; however, each group of activities also contains exercises that require no equipment and are suitable for the classroom.

• •

Lesson

1. Try to use at least one activity from each group of activities listed:

The first set of exercises called "I'm Small—Great!" is easier for smaller bodies.
- *Inchworm.* Assume a push-up position. Keep the legs straight and walk legs forward (hands stationary). When feet are close to hands, walk hands forward. Repeat. Decide if it is easier to be an inchworm with short or long legs.
- *Hang.* Jump up to a horizontal bar with palms away from face. Hang with feet off the ground. (Now teacher places hands on the performer's shoulder to add weight.) Decide if it is easier to hang with one's weight or with more than one's weight.
- *Over and Under.* Crawl over a box and then roll under a .3-m-high bench. Decide if it is easier to get over the obstacle and under the bench if one is small or big.

The next set of exercises called "I'm Big—Great!" is easier for bigger children.
- *Stretch.* While standing against a wall, extend arms and reach as high as possible. Decide if short or tall can reach higher.
- *Run and Leap.* Run to a line and leap as far as possible. Decide if tall or short can leap farther.
- *Leap Frog.* Squat down in a line. Others leap over the squatters by placing hand on the squatters' backs, spreading their legs, and jetting. Decide if it is easier to get over bigger or smaller people. Decide if big people or small people have an easier time leaping over others.

The third set of exercises is called "I'm Small—You're Big. I'm Big—You're Small. What Difference Does It Make?"
- *Jumping Height.* Stand facing the wall with arms stretched above head. Place a mark on the wall with a piece of chalk held in fingertips. Turn sideways to the wall and jump as high as possible. While jumping, swing hand upward and make another

chalk mark on the wall. Measure the difference between reach height and jump height.

- *Rolling Log.* Roll sideways the length of the mat. Decide if it makes any difference whether one is small or big.
- *Slow Run.* Run slowly around a course several times. Decide if it makes any difference whether one is small or big.

2. **Circle talk.** Praise each student's effort. Recall previous discussions of alike/different and tie the concept to today's lesson. God has made us all different. Note that certain movements were easy for some children and hard for others. Remind students of hard things they have already learned or are learning to do (riding a tricycle or bicycle, hopping, swinging). Perhaps tell them about a few motor skills that were, or still are, hard for you. Encourage them to practice the activities of this lesson during playtime.

3. **Student activity.** Have students refer to the Student Activity page in their workbooks. Read the words with the class and have the students complete the "I Can" sentence and draw an illustration of an activity that keeps them fit (for example, running, playing ball or tag, jumping rope, riding a trike or bike). If the circles are not precut, have students cut out the circle shape. Keep the completed activity pages in student folders.

4. **Closure.** As students finish up their activity sheets, ask volunteers to share what they have written. Then briefly summarize the lesson.

- -
Related Activities

1. Plan an ongoing "keep active" chart. Keep a record of the active games children play during recess or lunch hour. Or mark out a running or walking trail on the playground and encourage each student to use it. Record the number of times they walk or run the trail.

2. Enjoy the activity songs. Hop Palmer's "Posture Exercises" and "Exercise Every Day" from *Learning Basic Skills Through Music, Health and Safety, Vol. 3* are two suggestions.

LESSON 4: GETTING ENOUGH REST

Preparation/Materials
- Student Activity page

Objectives
- Students will identify rest as another human need.
- Students will recognize the importance of getting sufficient rest.

Background
Probably the hardest thing to get a child to do is take a nap or go to bed for the night. Children are not eager to interrupt their fun with sleep. Therefore it's difficult to get across the positive aspects of rest and sleep to this age group. Try to emphasize that we can enjoy the day much more when we have the energy to do the things we want. Being sleepy or tired keeps us from enjoying our activities.

●●●

Lesson
1. Sitting at your desk, tell students that this lesson is about something else people need to be healthy. Then yawn, stretch, and lean forward on your desk and pretend to go to sleep. Ask students to predict what the lesson is going to be about.

2. Ask questions about the purpose of sleep: "Why do you go to bed at night and sleep for a long time? Why do people take naps? Why do we sit down after we've been running fast or doing some other game?" Lead students to conclude that God made us in such a way that we (and other living things) need rest and sleep. Teach the meaning of the word *rest* (make sure students understand that sleep is rest). Explain briefly that during rest our whole body relaxes. We need rest (first graders should have from 9 to 11 hours of sleep each night) in order to stay healthy and grow properly.

3. Do one or more relaxing activities:

   - The children should get in a comfortable position in their chairs or on the rug. Then ask them to tighten and then to relax different muscles in their hands, arms, and legs. Next have them go completely limp. Finally, direct the children to close their eyes and imagine themselves doing things such as lying on a raft or boat moving in a gentle rhythm or stretching out in the warm sand and listening to the sound of wind and water.

   - Pretend to be hot air balloons, inflating and then deflating. Begin by being limp, saggy balloons with no air in them. Tell students that when you make a "shhhh" sound they are to gradually fill up with air. As they inflate, keep up a running commentary ("Shhh—You're gradually filling with air. Your legs are filling up, your arms, and now your chest.") Take your time and let the children really work at being filled with air. Then tell them when you make an "sssss" sound, they are to gradually let out the air. ("Sssss … sssss … sss. Are your arms and legs getting limp?") Allow children to slowly sink down onto the floor or their chair, before filling them up with air again. Continue the activity for an appropriate length of time.

4. Make up a song or sing the following song about needing sleep to be healthy. Use the tune "Are You Sleeping?":

> To be healthy
> To be healthy
> We need sleep
> We need sleep.
> Put your head down softly
> Put your head down softly
> Off we go
> Off we go.

Sing the first line of each pair of phrases for the class and have them sing the repeat. Other song suggestions: "Douglas Mountain" (*Raffi Singable Songbook*, no. 24, or Raffi's audiocassette *More Singable Songs*) or the first verse of "Father, We Thank Thee for the Night" (*Children's Hymnbook*, 54).

5. **Student activity.** Have students refer to the Student Activity sheet in their workbooks. Read the caption and have students finish the "I can" sentences. Then give them time to draw an illustration. If the circles are not precut, students should cut out the booklet page.

6. **Closure:** "To be healthy and well we need rest. When we have enough rest, we enjoy our activities more. And we're less apt to be crabby, too!"

• •

Related Activities

1. Integrate with an art project. Make small, individual pillows. (Students love these!) Use the pillows during the unit for various rest/relaxation activities. If possible, enlist a parent to help with the sewing.

Materials:
squares of cotton/polyester fabric the size of the pillow, two per student
filling for the pillows
textile paints (or perhaps fabric crayons)

Each student makes a pillow design (perhaps a daytime scene for the back of the pillow and a nighttime scene for front)

and paints it directly on the fabric (for fabric crayons follow directions on package). Sew up three sides of the pillow and then have students stuff them. Sew the pillows closed.

2. Read stories and poems about sleep. A few suggested book titles:
Bedtime for Frances by Russell Hoban
Ira Sleeps Over by Bernard Waber
Goodnight, Moon by Margaret Wise Brown
Bunny's Night Out by Roni Schotter
Still As a Star: A Book of Nighttime Poems compiled by Lee Bennett Hopkins

LESSON 5: FUEL FOR THE BODY ENGINE

Preparation/Materials
- Student Activity page
- Optional: make an audio recording of the story "The Body Engine." Ask friends or colleagues to read parts to provide drama.

Objectives
- Students will identify food as another human need.
- Students will identify two reasons why the body needs food.

• •

Lesson

1. Briefly review the health needs—exercise and rest—covered in previous lessons. Explain that as living things we also need food. Ask: "Why do we need food?" In discussion, lead students to understand that we need food in order to grow. Recall the lesson from Unit 4 on growing, and ask students to name parts of their body that have grown. Ask: "What is another reason we need food?" Tell students you're going to read a story that has the answer to that question.

2. Read the story "The Body Engine." Simplify or adapt the story as desired. Or if you have previously recorded the story, listen to it with the class.

The Body Engine

Jeff and Cindy Jones's father took them to the baseball game last night, and the trip there and back was so long that it made them very tired. Because they were so tired, they woke up late this morning and had to ride to school with their dad. When they were about halfway to school, the car just stopped … (Questions: Why do you think the car stopped? How many of you have ever been in a car that just stopped running?)

Mr. Jones got out of the car and lifted up the hood. Inside was the engine.

Jeff said, "I think that big engine is what makes the car go."

Cindy said, "If it makes the car go, then why aren't we going?"

Jeff said, "I don't know. Dad, why won't it go?"

Mr. Jones explained that an engine is not enough. The engine must be fed before the car can go. (Question: What do you feed a car engine?) (Gasoline, fuel.)

Mr. Jones also told Jeff and Cindy that there are many different kinds of engines, but that they can all burn their fuel to make heat and energy. Energy is what makes everything go!

Mr. Jones told Jeff and Cindy that people have engines too. Their engine is their body and it has to be fed. He asked Cindy if she knew what the body engine's fuel is.

She thought for a minute and answered, "Food."

Jeff said, "But Dad, how does the food make me move?"

Mr. Jones said, "It burns like the fuel in a car, only much slower and without flames. It may seem hard to believe, but food does burn in your body even though you can't see the flames. Feel your cheek. It's warm. The heat comes from inside your body, where the food you eat burns and makes heat."

Jeff thought again and said, "Can I eat just once and have enough fuel for always, Dad?"

Mr. Jones replied, "Well, Son, the problem with the car right now is that the fuel supply is gone because we used all the gas for the trip to the ball game last night. You see, a car can only hold enough fuel for a short time. Your body is the same way. If it doesn't get enough fuel, it will eventually stop running, so you must supply it with food fuel every day."

Cindy looked at her watch and said, "Dad, we're going to be late for school. Is there any way to get the car started?"

Jeff said, "Look Dad, there's a gas station right down the street."

And very soon the Jones car engine was filled with fuel.

Did you have your fuel for your body engine today?

Have the students answer the question at the end of the story. Repeat the question "Why do we need food?" (To give us energy.) Teach the word *energy* as new vocabulary.

3. Have students stand and move their body "machines." Start with small movements like wiggling toes and fingers or shaking heads; then raise and lower arms and or legs; finally do energetic movements such as jumping up and down. Explain that every body movement takes energy—some movements take a little energy, others a lot. Ask them to identify which of the movements used the most energy.

Recall the comparison in the previous unit of the body to a machine. Lead students to understand that just as a car needs gas to make it go, our body machine needs food to keep running; but unlike a car that can use the same kind of gas every time and run smoothly, we need a variety of foods to help us stay healthy.

4. **Student activity.** Read the activity page with the class. Answer the questions at the bottom of the page (Do you know where a fish/cow/lion gets its energy?). Have students identify what these living things eat for energy. Review that people eat foods that come from both plant and animal sources (taught at K level).

5. **Closure.** Summarize and evaluate with questions such as the following:
   • "What does a car engine need to go?"
   • "What do we need to go?"
   • "Name two reasons why we need food." (To grow and to have energy.)
   • "Why do we have to eat every day?"

LESSON 6: INTRODUCING FOOD GROUPS

Preparation/Materials

• Make 5 large "food friends" posters, one for each food group. Use magazine pictures, labels of cans, and/or parts of real objects (yogurt or cottage cheese containers, covers of cereal, raisin, or frozen food boxes; nuts, vegetable greens) to construct the figures.

• For student activity:
   magazines, old coloring books with food pictures
   construction paper, one large sheet per student
   five paper bags or boxes, each labeled with the name of a food group

Objectives

• Students will identify the five food groups and some foods belonging to each group.

• Students will be able to explain the specific contribution each food group makes to the body's health.

Background

Years ago, after assessing the daily dietary needs of most people, the United States Department of Agriculture formulated a food pyramid which included the eating of all types of foods.

The food pyramid was redesigned in 2010 to MyPlate. MyPlate is divided into five categories: grains, vegetables, fruits, dairy, and protein. The food groups are organized according to proportions needed each day in order to provide the body with the right amount of nutrients.

At the grade 1 level students learn the importance of eating from all the basic food groups because each is necessary for good health. To reflect current nutritional knowledge stress the importance of grains, fruits, and vegetables. Teach students that although our bodies need food for fuel and the nutrients of all the food groups for health, we do not need excessive quantities of food. Eating too much, even of good foods, particularly of dairy products and meats, leads to other health problems. We need to eat wisely—and in moderate amounts.

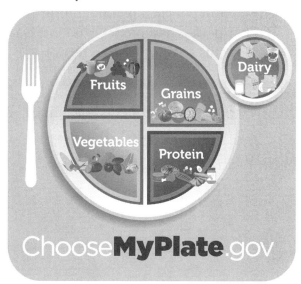

. . . .

Lesson (2 sessions)

1. Use the large posters of "food friends" to teach food groups. Stress that it is important to eat a variety of foods from each group because each makes a specific contribution to good health:

   - Grains (breads, cereals, pastas, pancakes, tortillas made from wheat, oats, barley, rice, rye, and buckwheat) to give energy for work and play
   - Fruits Group & Vegetables groups to keep our blood healthy and help build strong eyes
   - Dairy group (milk, yogurt, cheese, ice cream, cottage cheese, puddings, cream soups) to build strong bones and teeth
   - Protein group (includes both meat and plant sources—eggs, nuts, dried beans, peas, and lentils) to help the body build and repair itself

   Combination foods are introduced in grade 2, but you may wish to explain that some foods such as pizza or tacos combine several groups. If students raise questions about sweets or potato chips, consider saying these foods don't belong in the four groups, but can be eaten occasionally as extras.

2. Have the children each make a favorite food friend. First, the entire class should "go shopping" in magazines. Students should tear out pictures of food from the different groups and put each picture in one of the prepared food group bags. Then using the teacher posters as a model, students can use the pictures to create their own food friend. This second step can be done as a whole class or at a center.

3. **Closure:** "Today we learned about four food friends. Each friend helps us in a special way." (Elicit from students the names of the food groups. Recall the contribution of each group to good health.)

LESSON 7: EATING HEALTHY SNACKS

Preparation/Materials
- Student Activity 1
- Chart paper
- For class snacks:
  snack ingredients (ask parents to contribute)
  mixing and measuring utensils and plastic
    serrated knives as needed
  small paper plates and/or napkins, one per
    student
- Student Activity 2
- Optional: health puppets

Objectives
- Students will recognize the importance of eating healthy snacks.
- Students will thank God for the gift of food.

Background
Children at this age need energy foods at short intervals, so they need snacks. Of course, they also like to snack, so a good way to foster good eating habits in young children is to focus on healthy snacks. Although children don't plan meals, often they do choose snacks. In this lesson, try to target snack choices that contribute to nutritional needs, and encourage students to try some healthy snacks.

When you make the snacks in class, involve the students as much as possible in every step. Let them wash the vegetables and cut them up with plastic serrated knives, measure and mix ingredients, and help with the clean up. Consider dividing the class into small groups and have each group work together to make the recipe. Each child in the group should complete at least one step of the recipe. This is a good opportunity to reinforce concepts of cooperation.

Lesson

1. Have students look at the snacks in Student Activity 1 in their workbooks. Ask students to identify the snacks and to decide which of the food groups each snack represents. Brainstorm a list of other good snacks and identify which food group each belongs in. Consider writing the list on chart paper and displaying the chart in the room. Teach the word *nutrition* and make the point that snacks can be delicious and contribute to good nutrition. Stress that eating a variety of snacks is a good idea because each food is different and contributes in a different way to the body's health.

   Alternative suggestion: introduce the lesson with a dialogue between Terry and Sam. Terry is hungry; she wants chocolate cake for her snack. She tells Sam that she snacks on chocolate cake every day. She's made up her mind that chocolate cake is the only and the best snack in the world. Sam is surprised and lists all the different kinds of snacks he eats.

   Have the class talk about the situation. Ask "Are snacks a good idea?" (Yes. Young people need food frequently to keep up energy.) Make the point that a wide variety of snacks (and limited amount of sweet snacks) can contribute to good health.

2. Make and enjoy healthy snacks with the class. To keep the activity very simple, have a snack of fresh vegetables and fruit with yogurt dip or spread peanut butter on graham crackers. Or use one of the following recipes:

Crunchy Treat

1 cup honey	1/2 teaspoon nutmeg
1 1/2 cups powdered milk	1/2 cup raisins
1 cup peanut butter	crushed corn flakes
1 1/2 cups wheat germ	

Combine all ingredients except the corn flakes. Shape the mixture into small balls. Roll the balls in crushed corn flakes or chopped nuts.

Yogurt Pops

1 cup plain yogurt
1 mashed banana
1 teaspoon vanilla
1 cup orange juice

Mix well. Pour the mixture into 4-5 small paper cups. Place a wooden stick in each cup. Put the cups in the freezer until the mixture hardens.

Begin by writing out the recipes on chart paper, using simple illustrations on the chart so that the children will be able to read them. Teach new vocabulary. Have students copy the recipe so that they can make the snack at home, too.

Teach the health rule "be clean and careful" as the class prepares the food. Stress that children should wash their hands before working with food and that they should not use sharp implements.

As you enjoy the snacks, have students identify the food group each snack belongs to. Students who balk at eating unfamiliar foods should be encouraged to take at least a bite or two of each snack.

3. Celebrate God's good gift of food. Talk about why Christians pray before eating. Teach students the song "It's Good to Give Thanks." When students are familiar with the song, you may wish to substitute names of specific foods for the word *food*. Other appropriate songs are "Praise and Thanksgiving" (*Psalter Hymnal*, 631) and "To God Who Gives Us Daily Bread" (*Children's Hymnbook*, 51).

4. **Student activity**. Have students complete Activity 2 in the Student Workbook. Read the words together and then direct students to finish the "I can" sentence and draw their favorite snack(s) in the space provided.

5. **Closure:** "One way we can take care of our bodies is by eating healthy snacks. What are some snacks that you like that are healthy?"

Related Activities

1. Make a class recipe book of favorite nutritious snacks. Enlist parents' help and have students try out a recipe at home before submitting it for inclusion. Write out the recipes in rebus form.

2. Tell the story of Jesus feeding the five thousand (Mark 6:30-44).

It's Good To Give Thanks

Adapted from Scripture

Traditional
Arr. by Lyndell Leatherman

LESSON 8: PERSONAL GROOMING

Preparation/Materials

- Pictures of people practicing personal health habits or objects related to grooming habits (see step 1)
- Write the poem on chart paper.
- Student Activity page. (You may wish to precut the dotted lines in the tub.)

Objectives

- Students will identify the connection between good grooming and health.
- Students will be able to describe specific personal health habits.

Background

The origin of health education is personal health. In the early years of school health programs, personal health was the entire curriculum. However, more recently the trend has been to de-emphasize personal health. One reason is that most of the major contagious illnesses associated with personal health habits have either been eradicated or controlled.

However, this trend to de-emphasize personal health in health education is unfortunate. Take the mundane area of dental health, for example. Fully 97% of the students in our schools will have some kind of dental problems in their lifetime. Or take the topic of cleanliness. Reminders about daily personal health habits may seem to be a form of parental or teacher nagging, but students do need to be reminded that they can spread germs when they do not wash their hands before they eat or after they use the bathroom. Stress the positive side of personal health. Grooming habits such as bathing and brushing teeth and hair will help students stay healthy and clean and be more attractive. And they will like themselves better when they are healthy and clean.

Lesson

1. Display pictures of people shampooing, washing face and hands, brushing teeth, and sitting in tub or showering, or display objects such as soap, towels, shampoo, toothbrush (note: care of teeth is covered in next two lessons), comb/brush, fingernail clippers. Have students tell what the people in the pictures are doing or what the objects are for. As you talk about each, discuss why each personal health habit not only helps us look good but also helps keep us healthy. Explain that washing removes dirt and some germs that can make us sick; talk about why it is especially important to wash our hands before we handle food and after we use the bathroom. Ask: "What do you do to keep yourself clean?"

2. Lead the class in pantomiming various actions involved in personal health care. To make this more fun, accompany the actions with singing. Make up your own song or use the question and answer song at the end of the lesson (sung to the first four lines of the tune "Looby Lou").

   Make up more answers to fit the actions.

3. Display the poem chart and enjoy the following poem by Dorothy Brown Thompson:

> **Wish**
> If I could wish,
> I'd be a fish
> (For just a day or two)
> To flip and flash
> And dart and splash
> And nothing else to do,
> And never anyone to say,
> "Are you quite sure you washed today?"
> I'd like it, wouldn't you?

Elicit from the class the reason why adults check up on whether children have washed.

4. **Student activity.** Read the sentence on the activity page and review why keeping clean is important to health. Ask students to complete the "I can" sentence starter ("I can wash my hands" or "I can take a bath"). Then help the class to finish the booklet page by putting the "child" in the tub for a bath. Direct students to cut out the child figure. If you have not precut the bathtub's dotted line, show students how to cut along the line. (It may be easiest to have them fold the page on the dotted line and then do the cutting.) Students can then give the child a bath. You may wish to have them tape the figure in place (on the back).

5. **Closure.** Summarize the lesson and have students call out personal health habits.

• •

Related Activities

1. Read lesson-related books such as Vicki Cobb's *Keeping Clean,* Robert Munsch's *Mud Puddle,* or Gene Zion's *Harry the Dirty Dog.* Or show a film on the topic of cleanliness (see Lesson Resources listing).

2. Integrate with art and create illustrations for the poem. Or make a class booklet of the poem.

What Are We Doing Now?

Other suggested verses are:

shampooing/combing our hair
brushing our teeth
taking a shower
cleaning nails
changing our clothes.

LESSON 9: A LOOSE TOOTH

Preparation/Materials
- Student Activity page
- Story about child losing a tooth

Objectives
- Students will identify the function of their teeth.
- Students will be aware of the importance of taking care of their teeth.
- Students will understand the process of replacement of primary teeth with secondary teeth.

Background
These lessons on dental hygiene are based on the American Dental Society's curriculum *Learning About Your Oral Health.*

There are 20 primary teeth (8 incisors, 4 cuspids, and 8 molars) and 32 permanent teeth (8 incisors, 4 cuspids, 8 bicuspids, and 12 molars). Primary teeth begin shedding at about six years of age. Usually lower incisors are shed first, then upper incisors, lower cuspids, first molars, second molars, upper cuspids. Before primary teeth are shed, their roots begin to disappear (resorb).

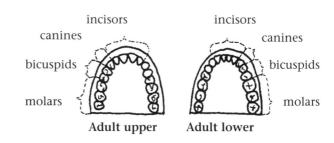

Lesson
1. Tell students this lesson is about one more thing they can choose to do to keep their body healthy. This choice has to do with taking care of one part of the body—the mouth. Have students guess what it is (taking care of their teeth.)

2. Briefly review the purpose of teeth (biting and chewing food, talking clearly, and having nice smiles). Students can feel the shapes of their teeth (the sharp front teeth are for cutting, the pointed teeth for tearing, and the wide back teeth for chewing. Demonstrate how we use our teeth to talk by making *s* or *th* sounds. Or have the children say the letters of the alphabet and notice which letters they use their teeth with. (Examples: the teeth touch for letter *c*, teeth touch the lower lip for *f*, and the tongue touches the back of the teeth for *e*.) Then have everyone show a smile to his or her neighbor.

3. Ask if any student has a loose tooth. Use the Student Activity sheet to explain the process of losing primary teeth and getting secondary teeth. Point out which are primary teeth and which are permanent teeth. Notice that permanent are "ready and waiting" to erupt. Consider using background material to point out the order in which primary teeth usually come out. Stress that it is important to take care of primary teeth because they guide the position of the permanent teeth. Have students label the primary and secondary teeth on the student activity page.

4. Read a story about a child losing a tooth. A good choice is the classic *One Morning in Maine* by Robert McCloskey. Other titles: Joanna Cole's *The Missing Tooth*, Lucy Bate's *Little Rabbit's Loose Tooth*, Pat Ross's *Molly and the Slow Teeth*.

5. **Closure.** Summarize and evaluate with the following questions:
   - "How did (the character in the step 4 story) feel about losing a tooth? Why?"
   - "Why do we need teeth?"
   - "Why is it important to take care of primary teeth?"

Related Activities

1. Create a chart on which students record each primary tooth they lose. Make a pattern of a tooth that students can trace and cut out. Have them write their name on the tooth and add it to a class mobile. Or make a "class mouth." Add one tooth each month. Children write their name on the tooth when they lose a primary tooth. Integrate with math by using information for a graphing activity.

2. Write a class story about a boy or girl who has a loose tooth. Include the different irritations of having a loose tooth and the feelings of the child when the tooth finally comes out.

3. Eating Fruit Roll-Ups (homemade or commercial) can provide exercises in cutting, tearing, and chewing with the teeth. Students can also make teeth impressions on the fruit leather.

4. Center idea: Provide animal jaws and teeth or pictures of them for students to examine. Have them predict what kinds of food the animal might eat by looking at the teeth. Construct a chart with matching flaps that conceal the answers.

LESSON 10: ATTACK ON PLAQUE

Preparation/Materials
- Student Activity 1
- For demonstrating brushing techniques:
  tooth brush
  model of mouth (borrow from local public
     health association)
- Student Activity 2
- Optional: letter to parent explaining booklet
- Stapler or two fasteners per pupil
- Optional: obtain dental kits containing
  toothbrushes, one per student
- Optional: construction paper cut in shape
  of activity page for back cover of booklet,
  one cover per student

Objectives
- Students will define plaque.
- Students will be able to identify the relation
  between plaque and cavities.
- Students will identify toothbrushing as a
  way to prevent cavities.
- Students will practice or identify tooth-
  brushing techniques.

Background
   Three primary teeth of the average six-year-
old child have been attacked by decay at least
once. And by age 21, the average adult has 11
decayed, missing, or filled teeth. So neglecting
daily personal oral care during youth has severe
effects. The chief problem in children's oral
health is dental caries—cavities.

   What causes dental caries? The American
Dental Association explains that a dental cavity
is not just a hole in a tooth. Rather, it is the result of a bacterial infection. Plaque, "a soft,
sticky, colorless layer of bacteria" that is constantly forming, sticks to the teeth. Then when
the person eats a food containing sugar, the
bacteria break down the food and change the
sugar to acid. After repeated acid attacks, the
tooth's enamel is penetrated, bacteria enter the
tooth, and a cavity results.

   Reducing sugar and starches in the diet is
one way of reducing cavities. But the problem is
not just the amount of sugar or starch. The
Dental Association stresses that frequency of
eating sugar-rich food, the length of time the
sugar stays in the mouth, and the physical form
of the food (such as sticky sweets) are all important factors in producing cavities.

   Of course, another way to reduce cavities is
to remove plaque from the teeth by brushing
and flossing. One of the best ways to educate
children about plaque is to use a disclosing solution (a harmless vegetable dye), so that they
can actually see the plaque on their teeth.

   Valuable resources for these lessons are local
dentists, hygienists, or community groups interested in school health education. They may be
able to provide a model for demonstrating
tooth cleaning techniques and other helpful
materials.

• •

Lesson
1. Recall the previous lesson and review with questions such as the following: "Why are
   our teeth important? What can happen to our teeth if we don't take care of them?
   What is one thing you can do to take care of your teeth?"

2. Use Student Activity 1 in the Student Workbook to illustrate of the chain of decay to explain why we need to regularly brush our teeth. Teach new vocabulary (including plaque and cavity). Explain that plaque is a soft and colorless layer (of bacteria) that forms on teeth. Plaque is left on teeth, it attacks them, and leads to cavities.

3. Ask: "How can we keep both our primary and secondary teeth healthy?" (Brushing, eating the right foods, going to dentist regularly, and flossing.) The rest of the lesson discusses the first three ways to promote dental health; grade 2 deals with flossing.

4. Discuss how eating the right foods can help keep our teeth healthy. Recall nutrition lessons. Stress that sugary, starchy, sticky foods promote cavities. Perhaps brainstorm a list of these foods.

5. Explain how to brush teeth. Demonstrate current techniques, or have a dental technician demonstrate toothbrushing to the class. (The American Dental Association suggests that "the thoroughness with which one brushes is more important than the specific technique used.")

6. Sing a song with the class about attacking plaque. Use the tune of "Twinkle, Twinkle, Little Star."

    > White teeth, white teeth, see them gleam,
    > When we keep them nice and clean.
    > Prevent decay the "clean 'em" way,
    > Floss and brush the plaque away.
    > White teeth, white teeth, see them gleam
    > When we keep them nice and clean.
    > Show Mr. Plaque that you're the boss,
    > Brush your teeth, use dental floss.
    > White teeth, white teeth, see them gleam
    > When we keep them nice and clean.

7. Ask: "Why should we see a dentist regularly?" Stress that dentists check on how the teeth are coming in and fix any cavities so that we don't lose any teeth.

8. **Student activity.** Use Student Activity 2 to complete the last page of the "I Can" booklet. Students should complete the sentence, connect the dots, and color the pictures.

    Assemble the booklets. If you wish, include a note to parents explaining the unit and the booklet. Send the booklets home after the review lesson.

9. **Closure.** Summarize and evaluate with questions such as the following:
    *   "What is plaque?"

- "What is a cavity?"
- "How can we keep our teeth healthy?"
- "What does a dentist do to help us have healthy teeth?"

• •

Related Activities

1. Show one of the following American Dental Association films: *Toothbrushing with Charlie Brown* or *Dudley's Classroom Adventure.*

2. Invite a dentist or dental hygienist to visit the class. Or read a book such as *The Berenstain Bears Visit the Dentist* by Stan and Jan Berenstain, *My Dentist* by Harlow Rockwell, or *Curious George Goes to the Dentist* by Margaret Rey.

3. Provide some dirt-covered rocks in a dish pan with water, toothpaste, and toothbrushes at a center. Students will enjoy practicing brushing.

4. Integrate a related sensory activity and math. Bring three flavors of toothpaste. Squirt small dabs of each on clean craft sticks or tongue depressors. After the students taste all three, let them vote for their favorite. Graph the results.

5. Mix up a batch of "Cornstarch Plaque." In a large pan, pour one box of dry cornstarch. Slowly add water (if you wish, tint with food coloring) to make a smooth, paste-like mixture. Allow the children to experiment with handling the goo (a unique sensory experience!). Talk about how what's left on their hands afterwards is much like plaque on their teeth.

LESSON 11: I CAN

Preparation/Materials
- Student "I Can" booklets
- Make a list of statements for playing Healthy Simon Says.

Objectives
- Students will review personal health practices.
- Students will choose to take responsibility for making healthy choices.

• •

Lesson

1. Use the student booklet to review the unit material. Talk about what the title "I Can" means (students can make choices that help keep them healthy). With each page review what the daily choices are.

2. Teach the class the song "Take Care of Yourself" by Jane Moncure. Have class members identify what health choices Danny, Betty, Sara, Tommy, and Susie make. Have fun singing the song and continue singing it during the next unit.

3. Play Healthy Simon Says. Give the class statements about health. If the practice helps us to be healthy, have students stand up; if it doesn't, have them stay sitting (if you prefer, have them clap for yes, and nod from side to side for no). Try a practice statement to make sure students understand the game. However, even if students make the wrong choice, have them continue in the game.

   Sample statements:
   It's healthy to eat lots of sweets.
   Be clean and careful when you cook.
   Eat healthy snacks.
   Make sure you don't cover your mouth when you sneeze.
   It's okay to go to bed late every night.
   We need to eat something from all five food groups each day.
   Cover your mouth when you cough.

4. **Closure.** Remind the students that God gives us the responsibility for taking care of our bodies. We CAN make choices that help keep our bodies healthy.

Take Good Care of Yourself

Jane Belk Moncure

Unit 6

Safety First

Goals

- Students will identify safety choices they can make.
- Students become safety conscious.
- Students will develop strategies and skills for self-protection.

Background

This unit covers several basic safety issues—traffic safety, fire safety, and stranger and child abuse education. The first two are straightforward safety issues. We all recognize that children must be aware of potential traffic and fire hazards and need to develop skills to protect themselves. But the last two areas—stranger and child abuse education—are also basic safety issues; students need help in those areas also. As much as we would like young children to remain innocent, in order to protect our children we must deal with the reality of danger and of sinful acts such as child abuse. Of course, it's important to take a balanced approach. Students must be informed, but care should be taken not to unnecessarily frighten them. Be matter-of-fact, and encourage them to develop self-confidence in dealing with all these issues.

Vocabulary

Integrate the following suggested vocabulary words:

safety	stop light	crawl	smoke	roll
accident	seat belt	low	number	operator
careless	stranger	stop	touches	rule
street	fire	drop	emergency	telephone
private parts				

Unit Resources

Davis, Diane. *Something Is Wrong at My House: A Book About Parent's Fighting.* Seattle: Parenting Press, 1984.

Winston-Hillier, Randy. *Some Secrets Are for Sharing.* Denver, Colo.: MAC, 1986.
   Both of these books deal with domestic violence. Davis's book addresses the problem of violent parental fights; Winston-Hillier's book addresses the problem of emotional and physical abuse of a child by a parent. These problems are not covered in the health program, but teachers may wish to use these resources one-on-one with students living with family violence.

KidsRights is a comprehensive source/distributor for materials on personal safety issues. For a catalog, contact KidsRights, 3700 Progress Boulevard, Mount Dora, Florida, 32757; phone 800-892-KIDS.

Lesson Resources

Lesson 2

AAA offers a variety of traffic safety materials available. One item of interest is a series of six single-concept cartoon films for primary grade level, which uses Otto the Auto to teach basic pedestrian, car passenger, and bicycle safety. Contact the local AAA office for a catalog or write to AAA Foundation for Traffic Safety, 1730 M Street, N.W., Suite 401, Washington, D.C. 20036; phone 202-775-1456.

Blakely, Cindy, and Suzanne Drinkwater. *The Look Out! Book: A Child's Guide to Street Safety.* Toronto/New York: Scholastic, 1986.

Bucklebear Team's Traffic Safety Series. Okemos, Mich.: Shinn.
> Consists of a wide variety of materials, all with a bear theme—teacher guides, videos, activity and coloring books, and posters. For a catalog, contact Shinn & Associates, 2853 W. Jolly, Okemos, Michigan 48865; phone 517-332-0211.

Chlad, Dorothy. *When I Cross the Street.* Chicago: Childrens Press, 1982.
> Alerts children to signals, signs, and traffic patterns.

Hall, Barbara and Doug. *Playing It Safe: Home, Summer, and Winter Street Smart Activities for Children.* Willowdale, Ont.: Firefly Books, 1990.
> Endorsed by the Block Parent Program of Canada, this activity book (intended for for ages 5-10) illustrates a variety of safety rules. Pages are reproducible for classroom instruction.

Hoban, Tana. *I Read Signs.* New York: Greenwillow, 1983.
> Large photographs of signs.

_____. *I Read Symbols.* New York: Greenwillow, 1984.

Leaf, Munro. *Safety Can Be Fun.* New York: Harper, 1988.
> This reprint of an "oldie" covers basic traffic safety.

Petty, Kate. *Stop, Look and Listen, Mr. Toad.* Toronto/New York: Barron's, 1991.
> Mr. Toad and his growing family learn how to cross the street safely. Not great literature, but the story gets the message across in an amusing way.

P.T.A. and the U.S. Department of Transportation. *A Safer Way for Everyday.* Mazer.
> An educational program to teach about importance of wearing safety belts

Lesson 3

Campbell, Louisa. *Ernie Gets Lost.* New York: Western Publishing, 1985.
> This Sesame Street book for grades K-3 is also available in audiocassette.

Chlad, Dorothy. *Strangers.* Chicago: Childrens Press, 1982.

Berenstain, Stan and Jan. *The Berenstain Bears Learn About Strangers.* New York: Random, 1985.

Fulton, Ginger A. *Saying NO to Mr. Stranger.* Chicago: Moody Press, 1987.
> The book, for ages 3-6, heavily emphasizes obeying parents as God's appointed caregivers and in particular obeying parents' rule to not go anywhere with a stranger. It defines strangers and presents situations for practicing saying no to a stranger.

Girard, Linda Walvoord. *Who Is a Stranger and What Should I Do?* Niles, Ill.: Whitman, 1985.

Holland, M., and J. Demers. *How Do You Know Who's a Stranger?* Pinellas Park, Fla.: Willowisp, 1987.

Too Smart for Strangers. Walt Disney Home Video.

> Intended for ages 3-10, this 40-minute film teaches children to say no to strangers who approach them, quickly get away, and report to an adult.

Lessons 4-5

Chlad, Dorothy. *Matches, Lighters, and Firecrackers Are Not Toys.* Chicago: Childrens Press, 1982.

Hamkin, Rebecca. *I Can Be a Firefighter.* Chicago: Childrens Press, 1985.

Hanum, Dotti. *A Visit to the Fire Station.* Chicago: Childrens Press, 1985.

Learn Not to Burn Curriculum: A Fire Prevention and Safety Education Program for School Children, Level 1. Third edition. Quincy, Mass.: National Fire Protection Association, 1987.

> Contains 22 lesson plans, lists of teaching aids, and fire safety information for teachers. *Learn Not to Burn* is being used in both Canadian and U.S. schools.

The National Fire Protection Association has a wealth of materials available: videos and filmstrips, activity and coloring books, stickers, and posters. For a catalog, contact the association at 1 Batterymarch Park, Quincy, Massachusetts 02269-9101; phone 800-344-3555.

Rey, Margaret. *Curious George Visits the Fire Station.* Boston: Houghton Mifflin, 1988.

> Both book and audiocassette are available.

What Do I Do When I See a Fire? Film. Quincy, Mass.: National Fire Protection Agency.

> In this 13-minute film, puppets teach about how to report a fire.

Lesson 7

Bahr, Amy. *It's Okay to Say No.* New York: Grosset & Dunlap, 1986.

C.A.R.E. Kit: A Sexual Abuse Prevention Program for Children Aged 5-9. Surrey, B.C.: Child Abuse Education Productions Association.

> A comprehensive, but rather costly resource, which includes a teacher guide with lesson plans, visuals for presenting key ideas, audiocassette and student book, and puppets. Write to the publisher: P.O. Box 183, Surrey, British Columbia V3T 4W8; phone 604-581-5116.

Carl, Angela R. *Good Hugs and Bad Hugs.* Cincinnati, Ohio: Standard, 1985.

> This activity book is a helpful teacher resource providing activities for reinforcing or expanding lesson ideas. Written from a Christian perspective, the level of individual activities varies considerably.

Colao, Flora, and Tamar Hosansky. *Your Children Should Know.* New York: Harper, 1983.

> Provides background information on the reasons for abuse and ways to prevent abuse.

Dayee, Frances S. *Private Zone.* New York: Warner Books, 1982.

> A read-together book about appropriate/inappropriate touching. It avoids naming anatomical parts and instead uses the term "private zone." It defines the private zone as special parts of the body covered by a bathing suit. Simple and clear presentation of basics for preventing sexual abuse.

De Moor, Ary, and others. *Child Abuse Education.* Part 3 of *Now You Are the Body of Christ: A Family Life Education Program for Christian Schools.* Edmonton: CSI District 11 Association and Grand Rapids: Christian Schools International, 1989.

Developed by the Curriculum Coordinator and five teachers of CSI District 11, this is a curriculum outline for teaching abuse prevention in kindergarten through grade 12. This valuable resource includes a sample protocol for reporting sexual abuse. Order from District 11 Curriculum Office, The King's College, 10766 - 97th St., Edmonton, Alberta T5H 2M1 or from Christian Schools International.

Freeman, Lory. *It's My Body.* Seattle: Parenting Press, 1982.
Intended to help children ages 3-6 identify uncomfortable touch and to give them the language to deal with "unwanted touching of any kind."

Girard, Linda Walvoord. *My Body Is Private.* Niles, Ill.: Whitman, 1984.
Sensitively written book covering types of touches, how to deal with disturbing situations, and telling adults about inappropriate touch. Ages 5-8.

Jance, Judith. *It's Not Your Fault.* Children's Safety Series. Edmonds, Wash.: Charles Franklin Press, 1985.
Including a read-aloud section, discussion questions, and background information, Jance's helpful book has two purposes: to assure children who have been sexually abused that they are not responsible and to teach all children the basics of preventing sexual abuse. The read-aloud story is about Terry and how she comes to tell adults about the sexual abuse of her step-grandfather. For ages 6-10.

Kehoe, Patricia. *Something Happened and I'm Scared to Tell: A Book for Young Victims of Abuse.* Seattle: Parenting Press, 1987.
Intended for the young child who is a suspected victim of sexual or physical abuse, this 26-page booklet is designed to encourage victims to speak out. Summary: in conversation with a kind lion, a child tells about being abused. The lion encourages the child to tell the truth and keep telling the truth until somebody listens, names people who may be abusers (including some family members), defines sexual abuse (naming genitals—vagina, penis, and anus), and helps the child recognize and deal with confused feelings. A direct, honest, and supportive approach.

Kraizer, Sherryll Kerns. *The Safe Child Book.* New York: Delacorte, 1985.
This book is intended for parents, but teachers will also find it helpful because of its concrete approach to preventing sexual abuse of children.

Lenett, Robin, and Dana Barthelme. *Sometimes It's O.K. to Tell Secrets! A Parent/Child Manual for the Protection of Children.* New York: Tom Doherty Associates, 1986.
Helpful for teachers as well as parents, this resource devotes five chapters to educating adults about the dangers and consequences of sexual abuse and about the importance of breaking the "barrier of silence" that surrounds abuse. Chapter 6 contains about 25 story situations which end with the question, What would you do?

Murphy, Elspeth. *Sometimes I Need to Be Hugged.* Weston, Ont./Elgin, Ill.: Cook, 1981.
A paraphrase of Psalm 84 for children.

Sanford, Doris. *I Can't Talk About It.* Portland, Ore.: Multnomah Press, 1986.
Annie, a child who is being sexually abused by her father, talks with God about her pain. Two noteworthy aspects: its sensitivity to abused children's tendency to blame themselves

and its stress on the need for forgiveness. Not suitable to read in its entirety in the classroom, but the book may be helpful for approaching a child who has been abused.

Plummer, Carol A. *Preventing Sexual Abuse: Activities and Strategies for Those Working with Children and Adolescents*. Holmes Beach, Fla.: Learning Publications, 1984.

Contains a skeleton outline of programs to prevent sexual abuse in K-6, 7-12, and programs for developmentally disabled persons. Other features: suggestions for setting up a prevention program and for involving parents, guidelines for instructors, and curriculum guides. A helpful teacher resource, but be aware that suggested roleplay situations require careful evaluation. Order from the publisher: P.O. Box 1326, Holmes Beach, Florida 33509.

Talking About Touching - Grades 1-3. Seattle: Committee for Children.

This material is costly, but comprehensive. It uses photos to elicit classroom discussion and covers physical abuse and neglect as well as sexual abuse prevention. Included are 46 laminated lessons, teacher guide, and parent activity sheets. For more information or to obtain a catalog of other materials, contact Committee for Children, 172 - 20th Ave., Seattle, Washington 98122-5862; phone 800-634-4449.

LESSON 1: DEVELOPING SAFETY AWARENESS

Preparation/Materials
- "Injured" health puppet, doll, or stuffed animal. Apply bandages, stitching, or "cast" to get the effect.
- Chart paper

Objectives
- Students will become aware of the need for considering their own safety and the safety of others.
- Students will identify safety rules for specific situations.

Background

Are accidents really accidents? About 85 percent of all "accidents" are the result of a person's action—or lack of action. The other 15 percent are the result of natural disasters such as earthquakes or hurricanes. People often shift the responsibility for an accident onto someone or something other than themselves. The car accident, they say, was due to the wet road, slick tires, or faulty brakes. In all likelihood, the driver was probably following the car ahead too closely or driving too fast for the road conditions, or simply failed to maintain the brakes. The natural tendency is to shift the blame for a safety problem away from ourselves. Children quickly pick up this attitude, so from a young age they need to be taught to take responsibility for their safety and the safety of others.

However, at this age other factors also enter in. Although grade 1 children usually have an overabundance of energy, their energy level is not matched by a corresponding amount of muscular coordination. In addition, they tend to act impulsively, without considering the possible consequences of unsafe behaviors. For this reason injuries due to falls, poisonings, and fire are common. In fact, most of the injuries for this age group are the direct result of such accidents. Thus teaching safety facts and behaviors is very important at this grade level. Recognizing which situations may pose danger and developing skills or strategies for dealing with dangers will help to prevent injuries and keep the young children safe.

Lesson

1. Show the students a health puppet, doll, or stuffed animal that has been "injured." Apply "casts" and bandages to get the idea across. Ask students what could have happened? Give students time to make guesses. If your classroom is equipped with a first aid kit, show the students the kit and its contents.

2. Tell students (or have the puppet tell them) how it was injured in an accident, but stress that the accident happened because of carelessness. Talk about ways in which carelessness can lead to accidents and injury both to ourselves and others. Perhaps tell or ask students to tell a personal experience with an accident related to carelessness.

3. Brainstorm attitudes and general patterns of behavior that can help to prevent accidents while playing at school, both in the building and outside on the playground (understanding that school rules help to prevent accidents, paying attention to what's

going on around us, listening to instructions, considering how what we do affects others, and so on). List them on the board. In each case ask students to identify what happens (or may happen) if they don't have that attitude or behavior.

4. Working with the class as a whole, develop a chart of safe behaviors:
   - daily home safety: storing toys out of walkways; being careful with electrical outlets, hot water, and handles of pots on cooking stove.
   - classroom safety: carrying scissors point down, keeping pencils and other equipment out of mouths and away from eyes, no running or pushing.
   - bus or subway safety: staying out of the roadway and lining up on the sidewalk, not pushing or shoving while boarding or getting off, staying seated on the vehicle, and no rough playing.
   - playground safety: following school safety rules for using equipment and areas of play. Include not pushing at the drinking fountain (to prevent knocked-out teeth).

   Illustrate the chart with sketches and post it where the class can see it. During this and the next unit, add other safety behaviors as they are taught. For example, after the next lesson add pedestrian and car safety rules. This could be a center activity with students illustrating the chart.

5. **Closure:** "Today we talked about things we can do to help keep both ourselves and others safe. In the next lessons we're going to be learning more about safety."

• •

Related Activities

1. For a thematic show and tell, have students bring in pieces of safety equipment used in various activities (sports, home repair work, and industry). Suggest items such as safety glasses or goggles, racquetball eyeguards, knee pads, gloves, masks, oven mitts, and dust masks. Demonstrate or discuss the use of each and explain why those who use the equipment are acting safely and responsibly.

2. Try role reversal. Have students pretend to be the parent, teacher, or bus driver. What rules would they make for the safety of all and why?

LESSON 2: STREET AND CAR SAFETY

Preparation/Materials

- Student Activities 1 & 2
- Make a traffic signal visual
- Chart paper or poster board
- Optional: an actual safety belt
- Optional: obtain block parent sign

Objectives

- Students will identify pedestrian traffic signs and signals and their purpose.
- Students will be able to explain pedestrian safety rules and the reasons for them.
- Students will be able to explain rules of car passenger safety.

Lesson

1. Have each student look over Activity Sheet 1. Begin by seeing how many signs they can identify on their own and then talk about what each sign or signal means and where students are likely to see it.

   Use the following rhyme to review the meaning of the stop light:

   > Red means stop.
   > Green means go.
   > Yellow means wait
   > even if you're late.

   Have the students color the signal signs in the appropriate colors.

2. Review basic pedestrian safety (taught at K level):
   - Walk on the sidewalk or grass away from the curb. Watch out for cars backing up in driveways.)
   - Cross the street at the corner. (This is an important rule; many children are injured each year because they suddenly enter the road from between parked cars or from behind bushes.) Stay in the crosswalk if there is one.
   - Look all ways for cars before crossing. Watch for turning cars.
   - Walk rather than run when crossing a street.

   Make sure students understand the reason for each rule. Write these basic rules on the board or on a chart to hang in the room.

3. Next, have the students refer to Student Activity 2 with the picture of the car with occupants wearing seat belts. Ask students to identify what each person is wearing and why. Explain the importance of wearing safety belts and also mention another car safety rule: don't distract the driver. Have students circle each of the seat belts.

4. Teach students the following safety belt song, sung to the tune of "Old MacDonald." If you wish, accompany the lyrics with appropriate motions.

Verse 1   Safety belts are not for jokes
Here's a safety tip
For yourself and for your folks
(I wear) it every trip (Substitute Mom, Dad, Sis, Brother wears).

With a click-click here
And a click-click there
Here a click
There a click
Everywhere a click-click.
Safety belts are not for jokes
Wear them every trip.

Verse 2   Everybody's wearing belts.
Now we're on our way.
(I'm) the first to click (my) belt
    (substitute Mom's—her, Dad's—his, Sis's—her, Brother's—his)
Click them every day.

With a click-click here
And a click-click there
Here a click
There a click
Everywhere a click-click.
Everybody's wearing belts
Now we're on our way.

5. **Closure.** Summarize the lesson. Refer to the visual and to the list of pedestrian safety rules and check up on students' understanding of each item.

● ●

Related Activities

1. Make tags to hang in the family car to remind the driver and passengers to fasten their seat belts. Students can make tags in different shapes (circles, triangles, rectangles) and decorate them with safety belt pictures or with slogans.

2. Contact the education department of the local police department and ask a police officer to give their traffic safety presentation. Or have your school crossing guards visit to review crossing rules.

3. Take a walk around the neighborhood to make sure students know what the various traffic signs mean. When you return to your classroom, have students draw any traffic signs that they saw.

4. Read books about traffic safety. *I Read Signs* and *I Read Symbols* by Tana Hoban, clear and colorful photography books, are useful in reinforcing the meaning of traffic signs. Other titles are: *Safety Can be Fun* by Munro Leaf and *When I Cross the Street* by Dorothy Chlad.

5. Play the game "Red Light, Green Light."

LESSON 3: SAFETY AND STRANGERS

Preparation/Materials
- Health puppets

Objectives
- Students will review the concept of stranger.
- Students will identify safety rules for dealing with strangers.
- Students will practice safe behavior in specific situations.

Background
Christians speak of having child-like faith— that is, believing without questioning. Children are known for their trust and confidence in every adult around them. Unfortunately, it is this quality that may bring children into grave danger with some adults.

It is very difficult to help children tell the difference between nice, helpful strangers and strangers who will hurt them. Children need to know that they will not be able to tell by appearance only which strangers are dangerous; therefore, they need to be taught (without causing undue alarm) to be careful about all strangers.

• •

Lesson

1. Ask: "Who is a stranger?" Lead students to understand that anyone they and their parents don't know is a stranger.

2. Discuss safety rules and strangers. To make the presentation livelier, have the health puppets discuss how to deal with strangers. Have one play "dumb," and the other provide information, or have them take turns presenting each point listed below.

   Ask students (or have a puppet ask them) to identify some helpful strangers such as store clerks and mail carriers. Tell students that even though most strangers are okay, because we don't know them we should be cautious around them. Emphasize the following points in the discussion:
   - Don't go anywhere with a stranger.
   - Don't take anything, including something you'd really like to have (toy or candy or pet) from a stranger.
   - Don't approach a stranger's car, even if he or she wants to give you something or wants you to help with something.
   - Don't go for a ride with a stranger, even though he or she claims to know your parents or claims to want to give you a ride home.
   - If a stranger approaches you, run to a nearby safe place or person for help.
   - Be sure to tell your parents or other trusted adult if a stranger approaches you.

3. Take the time to roleplay each of the above situations in which a stranger approaches a child. Play the role of the stranger yourself and have students take turns refusing your gifts, saying no, and telling another adult. Knowing what to do and being able to do it

in the actual situation are separate skills. Be sure every student has the chance to practice saying a firm, loud "NO!" to an adult.

4. **Closure:** "Today we talked about how to be safe around strangers. Most strangers are friendly and helpful, but to be safe we shouldn't go anywhere with a person we don't know—no matter how nice or friendly he or she may be."

• •

Related Activities

1. Read a book on the subject of stranger education to reinforce the lesson. Suggested titles: *Who Is a Stranger and What Should I Do?* by Linda Walvoord Girard, *Strangers* by Dorothy Chlad, *Saying NO to Mr. Stranger* by Ginger Fulton, *The Berenstain Bears Learn About Strangers* by Stan and Jan Berenstain, *How Do You Know Who's a Stranger?* by M. Holland and J. Demers. Or show a video on the lesson topic. *Too Smart for Strangers* is widely available.

2. Discuss what to do if you become lost. Read a book such as *Ernie Gets Lost* by Louisa Campbell.

LESSON 4: FIRE SAFETY

Preparation/Materials
- Student Activity 1
- Student Activities 2a & 2b
- Optional: make an audio recording of the story in the lesson.

Objectives
- Students will identify basic fire safety rules.
- Students will review the crawl-low-in-smoke procedure.

Background
The United States National Fire Protection Agency (NFPA) urges that students learn how to crawl low in smoke as a safety precaution because smoke is just as dangerous as fire. The agency explains: "Most casualties in fires are caused by smoke and toxic gases. Actually, flames and burns are responsible for the fewest number of deaths. More individuals are victims of asphyxiation, superheated air, and gases.... Thus, it is essential in moving through smoke in the evacuation of any building, including a home, to move rapidly in a crouching position below the visible smoke layer. If there is too much smoke to see the door, a person should crawl along the wall until the door is reached." By crawling close to the floor where the air and visibility are better, chances of survival in a fire greatly increase.

Students have been introduced to crawling low at the kindergarten level, but the procedure is repeated at this level because it is important for them to be very familiar with it.

• •

Lesson
1. Tell students a simple story about a fire in a home in order to get across the following fire safety rule: get out quickly, don't go back in, and get help from others. Embellish the following story outline with dramatic details. You may wish to tell it in the first person. Or if you have made an audio recording of the story, listen to the recording.

Sally's Doll
From the first moment Sally saw the doll she loved it. She loved the way it looked—like a princess. So she called the doll "Princess." And she loved the way it felt—soft and cuddly. Her grandfather had given it to her for her birthday. That was another reason why she loved it. She took her doll everywhere with her.

Early one morning Sally's mother woke her up. "Get up, Sally. C'mon, move quickly. We've got to get out of the house." As they went down the steps, Sally smelled smoke, and she saw her older brother hurrying out the front door. Quickly Sally and her mother followed him. The three of them quickly moved away from the house.

They ran next door to call the fire department. From the neighbor's house they could see smoke coming out of the kitchen window.

Suddenly Sally remembered her doll upstairs in her bedroom. She wanted to run back and get her doll. But her mother and her neighbors wouldn't let her.

The fire department arrived and put out the fire. There was a lot of damage to the first floor rooms, but not to the second floor. Sally's doll escaped "injury."

2. **Discussion.** Lead students to identify basic fire safety rules:
   - Get out quickly.
   - Stay out. Don't go back into the building. Even if the whole building is not on fire, smoke is dangerous.
   - Get help.

Tell students that although Sally smelled smoke, the smoke wasn't very thick when she and her mother and brother left the house. Ask what they should have done if the smoke had been thick? (Crawled low along the wall.) Why? (Because bad air in smoke rises to the ceiling, and good air stays below near the floor.)

Ask students about experiences they have had with smoke-filled rooms (or tell a personal experience). Have them identify common sources of smoke (campfires, grills, cigarettes, chimneys, etc.) and make a list of them on the board. Elicit from the class a description of the effects of smoke—burning eyes and coughing. Explain that if there's a fire at home, at school, or in any building there will be smoke, too; so they may have to go through smoke to get out. Again ask: "What should you do? (Crawl low in smoke to the nearest exit.) Why?" (Because bad air in smoke rises to the ceiling and the good air stays below, near the floor.) Have the students refer to Student Activity 1.

3. Practice crawling low in smoke. Because it may be hard to see in smoke, students should practice crawling along the wall to the exit.

4. **Student activity.** Have the students look at Student Activity 2a in their workbooks, explaining that these pictures illustrate the story of Sally and the fire. Ask students to identify what each pictures shows. Have them work in pairs to put the pictures in correct sequence. Then direct the class to paste the pictures on Student Activity 2b of the Student Workbook to "tell" the story.

As you review the completed sheet, stress the importance of leaving and not hiding during a fire and of not going back in to a burning building—for any reason.

5. **Closure.** Summarize the lesson. Encourage students to use the activity page to tell the story of Sally at home. Consider sending a note to parents suggesting they discuss home fire escape routes and procedures with their child.

• •

Related Activities

- Write the word *EXIT* on the board in red chalk. Teach students to find the way out of public rooms and buildings by looking for the exit sign. Walk though the school building and identify the exit signs. Ask students to look for the signs during the next week and report their findings to the class. Make a list of the places where they see the signs.

LESSON 5: STOP, DROP, AND ROLL

Preparation/Materials
* Student Activity page
* Gym mats (see step 3)

Objectives
* Students will identify what procedure to use if their clothing catches on fire.
* Students will be aware of the danger of clothing catching on fire.
* Students will practice "stop, drop, and roll" procedure.

Background
Learning the stop, drop, and roll technique can be important in saving lives and preventing serious burns. The U.S. National Fire Protection Agency claims that "many people have saved lives or averted serious burn injury" with the technique. In fact, NFPA says it "has documented cases where people have credited the Learn Not to Burn public service announcements featuring Dick Van Dyke with helping to save their lives. Of these reported 'saves,' the majority have been due to the stop, drop, and roll technique and crawling-low-in-smoke technique."

Why does the stop, drop, and roll procedure work? "Rolling smothers the flames by removing oxygen. Covering the face with hands prevents the flames from burning your face and helps keep heat and smoke from reaching your lungs." Be sure to stress that although wrapping oneself in a rug, blanket or large towel while rolling will help to smother the flames, only use these things if they are at hand. Don't run to get them.

● ●

Lesson

1. Begin by reviewing the fire safety rules of the previous lesson. Then recall that in the last lesson the class listened to the story of a girl whose house caught on fire. Ask students what they think might have started the fire in Sally's house, and lead them in a discussion of causes of fires. Include the following causes:
   * cigarette smoking—tossing cigarettes out of car windows, using ashtrays carelessly, placing partially burning cigarettes in trash baskets, falling asleep while smoking
   * playing with lighters or matches
   * not paying close attention to pans cooking on the stove
   * worn-out and frayed electrical cords

2. Ask whoever knows what "stop, drop, and roll" means to raise their hand. Call on a student to explain the procedure. Ask: "When do we stop, drop, and roll?" (If our clothes catch on fire.) Identify specific situations in which someone's clothes might catch on fire and specific safety practices to prevent such fires. (Standing away from a fire, avoiding rough play near a campfire, keeping sleeves of clothing away from flames on a stove.)

3. Use the student visual to and review each step of the procedure to follow if clothes start on fire.

- Stop: don't run.
- Drop: drop immediately to the ground and cover your face with your hands. (This action protects the face and keeps heat and smoke out of the lungs.)
- Roll: roll over and over or back and forth to put out the fire.

Explain that although wrapping oneself in something like a blanket or towel while rolling will help to smother the fire, they should never run to get those things. Stress that this procedure is only to be used in case of a clothing fire.

4. Have class members practice stopping, dropping, and rolling. Divide the class into three or four groups. Play marching music and have one student from each group march around the room or around the gym mats. When you stop the music, the students should say, "My clothes are on fire!" and practice the stop, drop, and roll technique on gym mats or on the classroom carpet area. Make sure they are covering their faces and rolling over and over. Continue the activity until all students have had the opportunity to practice the technique. (Adapted from NFPA materials.)

5. **Closure:** "Today we talked about ways fires can start. We learned that playing with matches or lighters is dangerous because that's one way to start a fire. We also talked about what to do if our clothes should ever catch on fire—stop, drop, and roll."

LESSON 6: DEALING WITH EMERGENCIES

Preparation/Materials

- Make a chart listing the emergency telephone procedure (see step 3).
- Toy and/or real telephones—if possible, both rotary dial and touch-tone
- List of class names, addresses, and telephone numbers
- Student Activities 1 & 2

Objectives

- Students will identify what an emergency is.
- Students will know the procedure for getting help in an emergency.
- Students will review their own addresses and telephone numbers.
- Students will practice calling in an emergency.

Lesson

1. Write the word *emergency* on the board. Ask children if they know what an emergency is. The class should understand that an emergency involves serious danger.

2. Ask: "What can you do if an emergency happens?" (Get adult help right away.) Identify ways to get help: quickly go to nearby adult or dial the emergency number. (Review that in case of fire it's important to get out quickly and telephone from a safe area.) Teach the emergency number in use in your area. Explain that those who answer the emergency number (usually 911 or 0) know exactly what to do in an emergency. If you use 0, explain that it stands for "operator," and it means that a telephone operator, someone working for the telephone company, is there to always answer the phone.

3. Use the chart to teach students the steps to follow in making an emergency call:
   - Give name.
   - Tell where you are (if at home, give own address). If operator asks, give the telephone number. Show students where telephone numbers are usually written on a telephone set.
   - Tell what the emergency is ("My mom fell on the steps, and my dad is at work").
   - Stay on the phone until the operator hangs up or tells you to hang up.

4. Demonstrate the procedure with a telephone.

5. **Student activity.** Have students write the local emergency number and their telephone number, name, and address in spaces provided on Student Activity sheet 1. A class list of names, addresses, and telephone numbers should be available for reference. As students finish this activity, have them use the worksheet to practice emergency calling (see next step). Encourage them to take the activity page home and review facts and the calling procedure with their parents. on Student Activity sheet 2, have students circle the pictures that represent an emergency.

143

6. **Student activity.** Give students ample opportunity to practice reporting an emergency with both rotary and touch tone telephones. Students learn best by doing. Enlist the help of parents or older students to help with this activity and check that students can use the telephone and know their own address and telephone number. Note, real telephones are preferable, but if they are not available draw both kinds of paper telephone dials for students to practice on. (It is important for them to practice with both rotary and touch tone models. If the child doesn't have much phone experience the numbers and the operation of a different telephone can be confusing.)

Note: Steps 5 and 6 are both good center activities.

7. **Closure.** Summarize and review with the following questions:
   • "What is an emergency?"
   • "What should you do in an emergency?"
   • "How do you make an emergency call?"

Praise students for work well done and tell them you have confidence that they can report an emergency if they have to.

• •

Related Activities

1. For additional practice, have students role-play emergency situations and practice telephoning to report the emergency. Suggestion: place slips of paper with the name, address, and telephone number of each student in a bag or box. Draw one piece out of the bag and read the address of one student. That student should quickly come forward and report a fire or other emergency on the phone. You can roleplay the emergency operator receiving the call.

2. Center idea: have available safety puzzles for students to put together. Make the puzzles from safety posters or pictures. Discuss the puzzles and the reason why the safe practice is important.

3. Collect and save newspaper and magazine articles about children who have successfully handled emergencies. To inspire students' confidence, read them to the class or make into a book.

LESSON 7: TALKING ABOUT TOUCHING

Preparation/Materials
- Student Activity page
- Teacher Visual (p. 167)
- For student activity:
  drawing paper, one sheet per student
  art materials—crayons, markers, or colored
    pencils
- Optional: pictures of people giving good
  touches

Objectives
- Students will differentiate between appropriate and inappropriate touch.
- Students will generate ways to protect themselves in specific situations of risk.
- Students will identify adults who can be a source of help.

Background
Some may question the need for child abuse education in Christian schools, but reliable research has shown that abuse does occur in Christian families and communities. And the rate of abuse is comparable to or only a little lower than that of the population as a whole. So although we may wish to believe that the problem does not exist in Christian communities, the facts do not support that view. Christian communities need to face the reality of abuse and help students develop skills for dealing with it.

Each level of the health education curriculum addresses the problem of sexual abuse. Since this is a sensitive subject, it is important for the school to contact parents or caregivers in advance and inform them of lesson content. You may wish to do this by letter or by meeting with parents. Your school administrator may prefer to hold a meeting to which parents of all grades are invited. Some schools discuss the content of child abuse prevention lessons at a parent orientation meeting during the first week of school.

Good communication with the home will give parents the opportunity to work with the school and to reinforce safety concepts.

The central focus of this lesson is safety, not sex education. In this unit students have been learning about safety. Now they are learning about one more type of safety—safety from sexual assault. Students who are aware of the danger of sexual abuse and know to protect themselves are less likely to become victims of sexual abuse.

To be effective, sexual abuse prevention education needs to cover the following basic areas in age-appropriate ways: (1) recognizing sexual abuse or differentiating between appropriate and inappropriate touch, (2) learning self-protection skills and techniques, and (3) identifying sources of help. We want to emphasize that presenting information on the subject of sexual abuse is not sufficient. Students also need to develop skills—decision-making skills and self-assertive protection skills. They must not only understand what inappropriate touch is, but must also understand what they can do about inappropriate touch.

It's also vital to present the material in a nonthreatening way. Introduce the topic of touch in a way that makes you and the class feel comfortable. Having the classroom teacher present the material is preferable because an atmosphere of trust and rapport has already been established. If you are unable to teach the lesson comfortably, however, consider asking another qualified person to teach it, perhaps another teacher on the school staff. This is an important safety lesson, and it should be presented in a supportive environment.

As you teach the lesson, be clear and direct; use correct names when referring to body parts. If a child should begin to report abuse during class (an unlikely event), talk with him or her later and consult with school staff.

● ●

Lesson

1. Begin by reviewing ways students have learned to stay safe. Be sure that the discussion includes safety with strangers.

2. Using the visuals, review the difference between appropriate and inappropriate touching (taught at the kindergarten level). Include the following information:

    God made all of parts of our body good. Some of our body parts are private. Private parts are our genitals and buttocks (preferably use correct words for body parts, but if you prefer, identify private parts as area covered by a bathing suit). Who may touch our private parts? Doctors, nurses, and other health professionals may touch private body parts for medical treatment. Parents may touch private parts when they are taking care of an injured area.

3. Discuss how to deal with and prevent inappropriate touch: saying no, going away, and telling a trusted adult about the situation. (Some children learn the slogan "No, go, and tell.") Help students identify people they could turn to for help (family members, pastors, teachers, neighbors). Stress that sexual abuse is always the abuser's fault and not the child's fault.

4. Describe a few What If? situations. For example:
    - "What if a stranger shows you his or her private parts?"
    - "What if someone wants to play a special game with you and asks you to take off your clothes?"
    - "What if he or she asks you to keep the game a secret or tells you not to tell anyone?"

    Work with students to think through the situations and plan clear and realistic responses.

5. Conclude that God wants us to touch each other in good ways. Tell students that most touches are good and show that we love and care for each other. Ask students to identify good touches. To make the discussion livelier, show pictures depicting good touches and talk about why we like these kind of touches. Consider reading Elspeth Murphy's book *Sometimes I Need to Be Hugged.*

6. Have students draw pictures of good touches. To spark ideas, talk about times when they receive or give good touches (hugs when they're coming home from school, holding hands with friends, baby brother's goodnight kiss). Have them write the caption "I like good touches."

7. **Closure:** "We need hugs and kisses and other touches from those we love. They make us feel happy. But sometimes touches give us an 'oh-oh' feeling. Then we should tell

another adult about what happened." If you wish, review lesson concepts by asking these questions: "Who may touch your private parts and when? What do you do if someone wants to touch your private parts?" (Say no, go away, and tell an adult.)

●●●

Related Activities

- Reinforce lesson concepts by reading books about appropriate/inappropriate touches. *My Body Is Private* by Linda Walvoord Girard is a well-written book with a balanced approach. *Private Zone* by Frances S. Dayee is meant for parents to read with children, but teachers will also find it helpful. Angela Carl's *Good Hugs and Bad Hugs: How Can You Tell?* is a good source of follow-up activities. Other titles: *It's Okay to Say No* by Amy Bahr, *It's My Body* by Lory Freeman, *It's Not Your Fault* by Judith Jance, and *The Safe Child Book* by Sherryll K. Kraizer.

Unit 7

Starting Right

Goals

- Students will become aware of individual choices that affect their health and safety.
- Students will take responsibility for making healthy choices.

Background

This unit continues to raise consciousness about health and safety issues and to make students aware of the important health choices they make daily. The unit also introduces students to the topic of substance abuse and lays the foundation for lessons at higher grade levels. We are all aware that substance abuse is a serious problem in North American society, and Horizons Health addresses the problem at each grade level. At grade 1 students are concerned with basics, distinguishing safe from unsafe substances, distinguishing between medicines and drugs, and identifying alcohol and cigarettes as drugs. They identify smoke in the environment and smoking, in particular, as detrimental to the health of their lungs, and they are encouraged to stay "smoke free."

AIDS—acquired immune deficiency syndrome—is not specifically addressed in grade 1. However, concepts essential to understanding AIDS are introduced. Students differentiate communicable from noncommunicable diseases, learn about one way germs are spread (droplet infection), and study wellness behaviors to reduce risk of infection. Higher grades build on this information so that students receive AIDS education in developmentally appropriate ways.

Nonetheless, because AIDS receives wide attention in the media, even very young children may be aware of AIDS and raise questions about it. Teachers must be prepared to answer their questions with age-appropriate information. The United States Department of Health and Human Services' *Guidelines for Effective School Health Education to Prevent the Spread of AIDS* (MMWR Supplement, January 29, 1988) suggests that education about AIDS for students in early elementary grades should center on allaying excessive fears and consist of these three concepts:

- AIDS is a disease that is causing some adults to get very sick, but it does not commonly affect children.
- AIDS is very hard to get. You cannot get it just by being near or touching someone who has it.
- Scientists all over the world are working hard to find a way to stop people from getting AIDS and to cure those who have it.

Vocabulary

Integrate the following suggested vocabulary:

sick	pills	poison	air
cold	alcohol	warning	medicine
germs	cigarettes	danger	immunization
symptom	lungs	drugs	pollution

Lesson Resources

Lesson 1

Berger, Melvin. *Germs Make Me Sick.* New York: Crowell, 1985.

Buchanan, Joan. *Taking Care of My Cold.* Windsor, Ont.: Black Moss Press, 1990.

Gretz, Susanna, and Alison Sage. *Teddy Bears Cure a Cold.* New York: Scholastic, 1986.

How to Catch a Cold. Filmstrip/audiocassette. Disney Educational Products.
    Running time of eight minutes.

Richardson, Joy. *What Happens When You Catch a Cold?* Milwaukee, Wisc.: Gareth Stevens, 1986.

Rockwell, Anne and Harlow. *Sick in Bed.* New York: Macmillan, 1982.

Vincent, Gabrielle. *Feel Better, Ernest.* New York: Greenwillow, 1988.

Wiseman, Bernard. *Morris Has a Cold.* New York: Scholastic, 1990.
    When Morris gets a cold, Boris thinks he knows what to do. Audiocassette available from
    KIMBO.

Lesson 2

Cobb, Vicki. *How the Doctor Knows You're Fine.* Philadelphia: Lippincott, 1973.

Lerner, Marguerite. *Peter Gets Chicken Pox.* Minneapolis: Lerner, 1959.

Marino, Barbara. *Eric Needs Stitches.* New York: HarperCollins, 1979.

Oxenbury, Helen. *The Checkup.* New York: Dial, 1983.

Pace, Elizabeth. *Chris Gets Ear Tubes.* Washington, D.C.: Gallaudet University Press, 1987.

Rey, Margaret. *Curious George Goes to the Hospital.* Boston: Houghton, 1966.

Rockwell, Harlow. *My Doctor.* New York: Macmillan, 1973.

Rogers, Fred. *Going to the Doctor.* New York: Putnam, 1986.

Ziefert, Harriet. *Stitches.* New York: Puffin, 1990.
    When Jon falls off his bicycle, he goes to the doctor for stitches. A read-alone book for ages 4-8.

Lesson 3

Drugs Can Be Dangerous. Filmstrip/audiocassette. QED Products.
    This filmstrip (seven-minute running time) teaches students about the danger of taking
    medications not prescribed to them and/or not given them by their parents.

Hawley, Richard, Robert Petersen, and Margaret Mason. *Building Drug-Free Schools. Part 2.* New
York: American Council for Drug Education, 1986.
    American Council for Drug Education's four-part drug prevention kit consists of three writ-
    ten guides and a film. Part 2, a curriculum for grades K-12, contains essential drug informa-
    tion for teachers and details the developmental basis for the schoolwide curriculum.

Helpful Medicines. Filmstrip/audiocassette. Topeka, Kansas
    A five-minute filmstrip, explaining how medicines help in case of sickness and stressing the
    importance taking only prescribed medicine.

Squeegee Learns About Drugs. Filmstrip. Marsh Film.

In a sound filmstrip (with guide and a 45-frame cassette) the puppet Squeegee talks about "basic safety rules for drug use."

Lesson 4

Chlad, Dorothy. *Poisons Make You Sick*. Chicago: Childrens Press, 1984.

Drugs, Poisons, and Little Children. Filmstrip/audiocassette. Educational Activities.

Reinforces the concept that sniffing, tasting, or ingesting any unknown substance can be deadly.

Poison Control Center. Contact local poison control centers for educational materials and take-home handouts.

Skidmore, Steve. *Poison! Beware! Be an Expert Poison Spotter*. Brookfield, Conn.: Millbrook Press, 1991.

Although intended for students in grades 2-6, this book may be a helpful teacher resource.

Watch What You Eat. Filmstrip/audiocassette. Topeka, Kansas

A seven-minute film explaining the importance of "knowing which foods to eat and things that may be bad for you like certain poisons."

Lesson 6

Canadian Lung Association. Contact the local branch of the association for educational materials.

Lungs Are for Life— 1. Kit. American Lung Association, 1983.

This excellent resource includes a teacher guide, activity sheets, colorful poster, and a cassette recording ("On the Right Track: The Adventures of Octopuff and Pollution Hound") and a read-along student booklet. Lesson 6 is based on sections 3 and 4 of the American Lung Association material. Contact the local branch of the American Lung Association to obtain the materials.

LESSON 1: CATCHING A COLD

Preparation/Materials

- Health puppets
- Plan a puppet script.
- A squirt gun or mister and piece of black paper to demonstrate how germs spread
- Make a discussion poster listing ways to avoid getting a cold (lesson step 4 lists the ways). Use magazine pictures or draw simple illustrations.
- Optional: write the poem on chart paper and make an audio recording of it.

Objectives

- Students will identify the symptoms of the common cold.
- Students will describe how cold germs spread.
- Students will understand and describe how they can prevent the spread of cold germs.
- Students will identify ways to protect themselves from illness.

Background

Children at this age are prone to upper respiratory diseases such as colds, sinusitis, and influenza. They may be more susceptible because their body's immune response is not fully developed. Because they are vulnerable to these diseases, it is very important to teach and practice ways to avoid spreading germs to others. Bear in mind that the typical elementary school classroom is conducive for spreading communicable diseases. Children usually sit close together in rows or in circles, and if they sneeze or cough without covering their mouth and nose, they can easily infect classmates. This is called "droplet infection." So throughout the school year reinforce the concepts of this lesson through practical application, through washing hands and enforcing the "cover your mouth and nose when sneezing and coughing" rule.

Lesson

1. Introduce the subject of illness by talking about an illness with which students are well acquainted—the common cold. Use the health puppets Sam and Terry to discuss the various symptoms of the common cold, the way cold germs are spread, and common feelings about having a cold. As an alternative option, pantomime having a cold and lead students to describe the symptoms.

   Script suggestion: Sam has a cold and is feeling miserable, Terry is the sympathetic and patient listener. Sam sneezes on Terry repeatedly while describing his cold symptoms: running nose, watering eyes, sneezing, headache, and sore throat. Terry can ask the class questions such as "What do you think is the matter with Sam? Have you ever had a cold? Did you feel like Sam?"

   Teach or have a puppet teach the meaning of the word *symptom*. (A signal from your body that something isn't right.) Give examples of symptoms of illness: (a fever, cough, or stomach pain). Then have Terry elicit from class a list of symptoms Sam has. Ask: "If you have symptoms of being ill, what should you do?" (Tell an adult about it.)

2. **Discussion.** Ask: "How do you think Sam got his cold?" (Students may say from germs.) Explain that diseases are caused by germs, tiny things that we can't see with our eyes alone, but that are all around us. Different kinds of germs cause different illnesses. When germs get into our bodies they can make us sick. Our bodies keep out germs in several ways.
   - Skin protects us.
   - Tiny hairs in our nose stops germs.
   - Wetness inside of the mouth and throat traps germs.

   Brainstorm some ways germs can enter the body (include sharing utensils or entering through cuts and scrapes in the skin).

   Stress that even when germs do enter the body, we don't always get sick. When we are healthy we can fight off germs. But if we haven't gotten enough rest or exercise or eaten healthy foods, sometimes our bodies can't fight them off, and then we get sick.

3. Display the poem chart and read the following poem by Jack Prelutsky with the class:

   Sick
   Hot, cross, aching head,
   Prickly, tickly, itchy bed.
   Piles of books and toys and puzzles
   Heavy on my feet,
   Pillows thrown all anyhow,
   Wrinkles in the sheet.
   Sick of medicine, lemonade,
   Soup spooned from a cup.
   When will I be *better?*
   When can I get *up?*

   Elicit from students how the child in the poem is feeling and why. Talk about how illness affects our feelings. How is the child's family trying to cheer up him or her? If time permits, let children share special family rituals during illness or pantomime the poem.

4. Use a discussion poster to teach ways to avoid getting a cold. Have students identify what's going on in each picture and how the behavior helps to guard against getting sick. Include the following behaviors:
   - dressing appropriately in cold or wet weather
   - eating a variety of nutritious food
   - getting enough sleep
   - getting regular exercise
   - not getting too close to people with colds
   - not using same drinking glasses, etc., as others
   - washing hands before eating or handling food

   (Immunizations will be added in the next lesson.)

5. Ask: "And how can we keep from spreading our germs to others?" (Cover our mouth when we cough and covering our mouth and nose when we sneeze.) Demonstrate droplet infection by spraying water with a squirt gun or plant mister against a piece of black paper (a repeat of kindergarten level demonstration).

6. **Closure:** "Today we talked about how we feel when we're sick and what we can choose to do to keep germs from spreading." Refer to the poster and perhaps note that displaying the poster will help remind the whole class of healthy choices.

• •

Related Activities

1. Listen to "Cover Your Mouth" from Hap Palmer's *Learning Basic Skills through Music,* vol. 3.

2. Reinforce lesson concepts with films and books. Use a filmstrip such as "How to Catch a Cold" or read *Germs Make Me Sick* by Melvin Berger, *Teddy Bears Cure a Cold* by Gretz and Sage, *What Happens When You Catch a Cold?* by Joy Richardson, *Taking Care of My Cold* by Joan Buchanan, *Morris Has a Cold* by Bernard Wiseman, or the light-hearted *Feel Better, Ernest* by Gabrielle Vincent.

3. Center idea: complete-the-sentence strips. Write sentences dealing with material covered in this unit on strips of posterboard. Leave blanks in the sentences for students to fill in. Provide vocabulary cards (use new unit vocabulary) with the necessary words. Students can choose the correct word to complete each sentence. Store the sentences and word cards in a large envelope. Add sentences with new vocabulary as the unit progresses.

4. Create a class booklet illustrating the poem "Sick." Put the booklet and an audio recording of the poem at the book center for students to enjoy.

LESSON 2: IMMUNIZATIONS AND HEALTH CHECKUPS

Preparation/Materials
- Story about a health checkup to read to the class
- Pictures of health professionals
- Optional: beanbag
- For student activity:
  Student Activity sheet
  cardboard rolls, one per student

Objectives
- Students will identify ways to prevent communicable disease from spreading.
- Students will differentiate between communicable and noncommunicable diseases.
- Students will understand that immunizations protect them from communicable disease.

Background

Another way students can remain healthy, besides personal health behaviors, is through regular health checkups. Fortunately, the "crisis intervention" approach to visiting the doctor is no longer the norm, for through regular checkups and carefully scheduled immunizations some illnesses can be prevented and others can be spotted early.

• •

Lesson

1. Lead students to discuss other illnesses they have had besides colds (most common examples are chicken pox and flu).

2. Teach the meaning of the term "communicable disease." (Any disease that can be "caught" from someone who has it.) Mention a few noncommunicable diseases with which students may be familiar such as allergies or asthma. Consider showing the class how communicable diseases travel from one to another by having class members toss a bean bag (representing an illness) from one to another.

3. Briefly review the previous lesson's chart of how to avoid spreading communicable disease. Tell the class that there is one more way not on the list—getting immunizations. Teach the word *immunization* and explain that immunizations help our body fight germs. Consider describing how immunizations lead the body to develop antibodies to fight the germs.

4. Ask students who gave them their shots. Show the pictures of health professionals and have students identify them as health helpers.

5. Read an appropriate story about a health checkup or a visit to doctor's office. Suggested titles: *The Checkup* by Helen Oxenbury, *How the Doctor Knows You're Fine* by Vicki Cobb, *My Doctor* by Harlow Rockwell, or *Going to the Doctor* by Fred Rogers. Discuss the story. What did the doctor do to promote health?

6. **Student activity.** Tell students they're going to make health helper puppets. Have them select pieces to form puppets of choice. Direct them to color the pieces, cut them out, and paste them on a cardboard roll. The class can use the puppets to act out how health professionals help prevent the spread of communicable diseases.

7. **Closure.** Use the following questions to summarize the lesson:
   - "What is a communicable disease?"
   - "What are immunizations? How can they help keep us healthy?"
   - "Why are regular health checkups important?"

● ●

Related Activities

1. Have the school nurse or public health nurse talk to the students about immunizations and the need for regular health checkups.

2. Talk about going to the hospital. Read *Curious George Goes to the Hospital* by Margaret Rey, *Eric Needs Stitches* by Barbara Marino, or *Chris Gets Ear Tubes* by Elizabeth Pace.

3. Read the classic *Peter Gets the Chicken Pox* by Marguerite Lerner.

LESSON 3: MEDICINES AND DRUGS

Preparation/Materials
- Student Activity page

Objectives
- Students will review the concept that they should never take medicines on their own.
- Students will decide not to ingest any unknown substance without checking with their adult caregiver.

Background

Children of this age are often confused about the differences between a drug and a medicine. To make the distinction clear, at the primary grade level Horizons Health defines *medicine* as a substance used specifically to treat a symptom and to cure or prevent a disease and defines a *drug* as an illegal substance that chemically alters the state or condition of the body and/or mind. The stress in this lesson, however, is simple: don't take any unknown substance.

Why begin drug education at such a young age? One purpose is to protect children by preparing them to deal with situations that are all too common in our society. Another goal is to help students form correct attitudes toward drugs from the beginning.

• •

Lesson

1. **Discussion.** Begin by talking about the following questions:
   - What is a medicine? (Something that helps us get better when we're sick.)
   - Who should give you medicine? (Doctors, nurses, parents, or another adult caregiver.)

   Contrast *medicines* taken by those who are ill and *drugs* used by those who are healthy to make them feel different. Have students identify some medicines they have taken.

   Teach the word *drugs* and lead students to talk about what they know about drugs. Explain that drugs may make people feel good for a while, but then they can make people very sick.

2. Refer the students to the Student Activity sheet in the Student Workbook. Ask students to identify the pictures. Briefly explain the health risks involved with each drug. Alcohol and other drugs can make people think and act differently. When people take too much alcohol and take other drugs they can't always see straight or react quickly. Then they sometimes cause accidents. When some people take alcohol and other drugs, they can't stop taking them. Then they need special help to get well again. Cigarettes have a drug called nicotine in them. The smoke of cigarettes isn't healthy for our lungs, so smoking for a long time can make people sick (Lesson 6 addresses smoking in more detail). Since students may have heard about drugs on TV or from other sources, take time to answer their questions and clear up possible confusion on the subject of drugs. Have the students color the large X over each picture.

3. Consider a few What If? situations. For example:
   - "What if you're playing in the park and you find something that looks like 'candy'?"
   - "What if an older student on the playground offers to give you a pill or a drink that will make you feel great?"
   - "What if you're at the beach on a hot day and you're really thirsty? You see a half-filled pop bottle."

   Lead them to decide to avoid taking any unknown substance without checking with a parent or other responsible adult caregiver.

   Have the students roleplay the situations, giving everyone the opportunity to say no.

4. **Closure:** "Today we talked about the difference between medicine and drugs." (Elicit what the difference is.)

●●

Related Activities

1. Distinguish between over-the-counter medications and prescription medications.

2. View and discuss a filmstrip on the lesson topic. *Helpful Medicines, Squeegee Learns About Drugs,* or *Drugs Can Be Dangerous* are suggested films.

LESSON 4: BEWARE! POISON!

Preparation/Materials
- Student Activity page
- For class book on edible/inedible substances:
  construction paper
  magazines
- Optional: an empty, clean container with poison label

Objectives
- Students will review meaning of warning symbols/words.
- Students will identify common household poisons.
- Students will differentiate between edible and inedible substances.

• •

Lesson

1. Show students the Student Activity and the container with the poison symbol. Ask students: "What does this sign mean?" Review the meaning of the symbol (taught at the Kindergarten level). Teach the words *danger, poison, warning.*

2. Review the concept that students should never taste or swallow an unknown substance. Some containers don't carry a warning sign, but may, nonetheless, be poisonous substances. If the children are not sure, they should always "ask before tasting." If there is no one to ask, they should not eat or taste the substance.

3. As a class, make a list of some common household substances that should never be ingested. To help students think of specific items, ask them to imagine, for example, that they are in their garage at home. What poisons could be in the garage? (Antifreeze, paint, turpentine, plant food, windshield washer solvents, gasoline, garden sprays, car care products.) In the bathroom? (Medicines, nail polish, nail polish remover, rubbing alcohol, bathroom bowl cleaners, cleansers, shaving lotion, colognes, iodine, cough syrup and other cold medications, bubble bath, hair spray, hair dye.) In the kitchen? (Vitamins, cleansers, disinfectants, oven cleaner, dishwasher detergents, bleach, drain cleaners, furniture polish.) Again, stress that although these items do not carry special warning signs, they are dangerous if ingested. Note that sometimes adults may use empty food containers to store cleaning products or other substances that would be poisonous. Note, too, that house plants are nice to look at, but they can be poisonous.

4. Make a class book differentiating edible and inedible substances. Have students cut out pictures from magazines and paste them on construction paper. Then they should write appropriate captions such as the following: "Eat me. I'm food." Or "Don't eat me. I'm poison." Consider having them add the symbol of a red circle with diagonal line across it on the inedible items. Put the student papers together make a book for students to look through. This is a good center activity.

5. **Closure.** Ask volunteers to tell one thing they learned from the lesson. Perhaps end by chanting together the captions used in step 4.

● ●

Related Activities

1. Make the class list of common household items that are potential poisons as complete as possible. For example, add poisonous house plants to the list. Send copies of the list home with the students with the suggestion that they together with their parents go through the house and label any poisonous substances. Households with young children should put poisons out of reach and locked away.

2. Contact the local poison control center for educational materials to reinforce the lesson. Videos, stickers to put on household poisons, and lists of poisons are usually available.

3. Read *Poisons Make You Sick* by Dorothy Chlad or appropriate materials available from the local poison control center.

LESSON 5: SAFETY REVIEW— SUBSTANCE ABUSE/POISON

Preparation/Materials
- For lesson activity:
  pictures cut from catalogs or magazines of a variety of safe and unsafe objects (foods, alcohol, tobacco products, medicines, drugs, paints, matches, toys, sports equipment, books)
  squares of tagboard, one for each picture
  two boxes, one labeled "Safe" and the other "Dangerous"
  Make a set of safe/unsafe cards for students to sort by mounting each picture on a square of tagboard.
- Student Activity page

Objectives
- Students will distinguish between safe and dangerous objects.
- Students will review concepts of previous two lessons.

Background
The material for this lesson is adapted from the curriculum of *Building Drug-Free Schools* (American Council for Drug Education, 1986).

Lesson

1. Show students the picture of safe/unsafe objects one at a time (or have students choose one to show). Have the class identify what it is and through discussion decide whether the object is safe or dangerous for them. Elicit the reasons for their judgment. Then place the picture in the "Safe" or "Dangerous" box.

   Make sure students know why the object is unsafe and in what way it is unsafe. They should make their judgments about safe/unsafe based on what is safe for *them* to use. So, for example, not only items like matches and poisons should be judged unsafe, but also all medicines, tobacco products, and alcohol.

2. Reinforce safety concepts with a chant. For example:

   Be safe.
   Be safe.
   Don't taste (Hold up picture card of an item and have students name it).

   When appropriate, substitute the word *use* for *taste*. If the picture is of edible item, drop the word *don't*. Again, stress that students shouldn't sample anything questionable without checking with an adult.

3. **Student activity.** Tell students that owls are thought to be one of the wisest of animals. Now that they know how to be safe and ask before tasting, they deserve a wise owl award. Distribute the certificates and have each student fill in his or her name and write "Ask first" in the space provided. If time permits, have them color the owl.

4. **Closure:** "Wise owls will use what they've learned. How can you use what you've learned?" (To stay safe and help others stay safe by following the safety rule.)

• •

Related Activities

1. Show a video or filmstrip such as *Drugs, Poisons, and Little Children* or *Watch What You Eat* to reinforce the concept that tasting or ingesting unknown substances is dangerous.

2. Write a class story about someone who makes safe decisions about using some of the items discussed in the lesson.

3. Put the picture cards of safe/unsafe objects in a center for students to sort.

LESSON 6: CLEAN AIR FOR ME

Preparation/Materials
- Two chalk-filled board erasers
- One or more objects for illustrating what air does (see step 2):
  paper airplane or glider
  blow dryer and lightweight object to move
     or cloth with wet spot
  balloon
  bubble wand and suds
  pinwheel
  fan
- For drawing outline of child and lungs:
  mural paper, enough to draw outline of one
     student
  markers, two colors
- Empty cigarette package

- Optional: visual of lungs from Unit 4, Lesson 5

Objectives
- Students will understand the role of air in breathing.
- Students will understand the importance of clean air.
- Students will be aware of the effects of smoking on our lungs.
- Students will choose not to start the habit of smoking.

Background
This lesson is based on *Lungs Are for Life—1* published by the American Lung Association.

• •

Lesson

1. Begin by making the class aware some of the uses of air. Ask: "Can we see air? Can you touch air? Can we feel air?" Explain that even though we can't see or touch air, it is all around us, and sometimes when air blows, we can feel it. Air, something we take for granted, is an important part of God's creation.

2. Illustrate some things air does. Suggestions: fly a paper airplane or glider; operate a toy pinwheel; blow (or use a blow dryer) to move lightweight objects—seeds, twigs; blow bubbles from a bubble wand; dry a wet spot on cloth with blow dryer; inflate a balloon; tie a balloon to a string and hold it in front of a fan. Ask students to identify what the air is doing (for example, pushing, holding up, filling, drying). Finally, have the whole class jog in place or take some deep breaths. Ask students what makes their chest go up and down when they breathe deeply; then identify one more use of air—humans need air to stay alive.

3. Trace the outline of one child on a piece of mural paper (with child lying on back with face to the side—see sketch following). Ask: How does air get into our lungs? Give students opportunity to answer and then draw in the windpipe and lungs on the figure. Explain that air consists of several gases—one of these is oxygen. When we breathe in, we take oxygen into our bodies. The oxygen changes the food we eat into energy. And we know that we need energy to move our bodies and for other things. We breathe out

what is left. (Explain this is also a gas—carbon dioxide). Tell students that breathing clean air is important for our health.

With a colored marker trace the pathway of air being breathed in. Explain that we breathe in through the mouth or nose. The air goes through the windpipe and down into our lungs. Use a marker of a different color to show air being exhaled.

4. Discuss and demonstrate air pollution. Teach the term *pollution* and have the class work together to make a list of common causes of air pollution (car exhaust, factory smoke, burning trash and leaves, spraying with pesticides, cigarette smoke). The American Lung Association suggests that the teacher clap two chalk-filled board erasers together to demonstrate air pollution.

5. Discuss the possible effects of cigarette smoke on the lungs. Ask: "What do you think breathing in smoke from a cigarette or pipe could do to the lungs? (Cause coughing, make lungs dirty, damage the lungs.) Do you think smoking is healthy?" Note that a smoker spends a lot of time breathing polluted air. Show students the warning on the cigarette package.

6. Review the Unit 5 concept of the God-given responsibility to make healthy choices. Stress that once people start smoking, it's very hard for them to quit. Since smoking is not healthy, it's better not to start smoking.

7. Write a class story about the effects of smoking. Consider writing it from the point of view of a smoker's lungs, and give the lungs a name such as Lily or Louie Lung.

8. **Closure.** Ask: "Why is smoking unhealthy? Why is it better not to start smoking?"

Related Activities

1. Ask the local Cancer Society or Lung Association to demonstrate how smoking fouls the lungs.

2. Brainstorm ways people can help to keep the environment pollution free. Explain why Christians should care for the environment: God gave people the task to take care of the world.

3. The American Lung Association suggests you take pictures of your class working through this lesson and write a news article (ask students for suggestions). Then send the article to the local newspaper or to the local office of the Lung Association.

LESSON 7: CULMINATING LESSON

Preparation/Materials
- Student Activity page
- Song "Take Care of Yourself" (Unit 6, Lesson 11) and other songs of choice
- Health puppets or puppets and props for students
- Plan a script for puppet play or skit.

Objectives
- Students will review health concepts.
- Students will decide to make healthy choices.

• •

Lesson
Select from the following activities:

1. Use the activity page to review health choices. Talk about each health choice and have students check the box that shows how they are doing. Make clear that their responses do not have to be shared. In the empty spaces add other health choices stressed during health in the past year. Elicit from students ways they can improve their record.

2. Sing the song "Take Care of Yourself" and other songs included in the health curriculum. You may also wish to make up a piggyback song about the choices listed on the activity page. (For example, "I will brush my teeth each morning (each evening) / Yes, I will" to the tune of "Comin' Round the Mountain.")

3. Give a skit or puppet play about health choices covered during the year. You may want to have Sam and Terry present some of the main points covered in health or listed on the activity page. Have them engage students in a conversation (for example, "When do you feel happy/sad/afraid/angry?"). Then have the puppets say a fond farewell and encourage students to make good health choices.

   Another option is to have students give a skit or puppet play for other class members, parents, or other classes. In the presentation you could include scenes on the following topics:
   - Getting along with others
   - We feel (happy, sad, afraid, angry) when. . .
   - Minding our manners
   - Eating right
   - Keeping fit
   - My body machine
   - Fire!
   - Looking both ways

Close the program by singing favorite health songs.

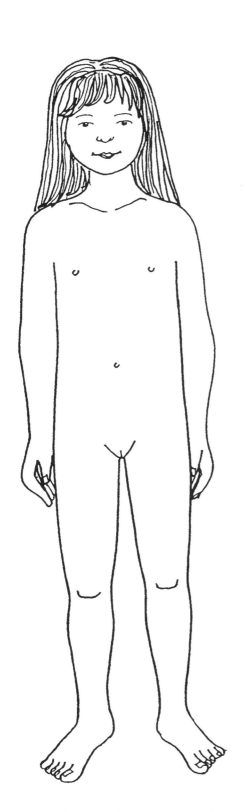
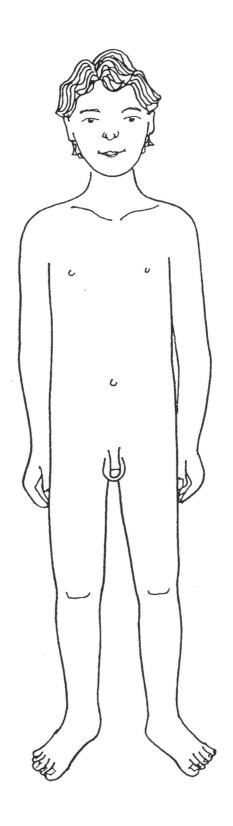

Permission granted to reproduce this page only.